Complete H

Gillian Pearkes has had .... all her life, particularly fruit of many types, and trees, shrubs and garden plants. This led to the planting of a commercial vineyard in 1976 at Bickleigh, near Tiverton in Devon, on a hillside called Yearlstone. She also planted a professional cider apple orchard at Yearlstone in 1983, where many ancient and modern varieties are now starting to bear well.

The vineyard produces three fine elegant white wines and a full mellow red wine, all under the Yearlstone label. Apart from the professional vineyard there is an area devoted to varietal trials, and to research into the culture and cropping potential of the ever increasing number of varieties, which is of considerable value to the growing wine producing industry in England. This is the largest varietal collection in England, with vines from all over the world.

Gillian Pearkes was awarded a Nuffield travelling scholarship in 1976 and 1977 to further her studies in France, Germany and Luxembourg. In 1984 she was invited to speak at the first International Conference for Cool Climate Viticulture in Eugene, Oregon, where she read a paper on the potential of all vine varieties currently grown in Britain. While in the USA she visited many vineyards and growers in California, Oregon and Washington, and also in British Columbia in Canada.

Gillian runs courses for new winegrowers at Yearlstone, where the most up to date worldwide viticultural practices are explained alongside a full practical programme for planting, training, pruning, spraying and cropping vines. Harvest and winemaking are the subject for the final seminar of each course, where participants are instructed by Gillian and her brother, Tim. These courses are always well attended.

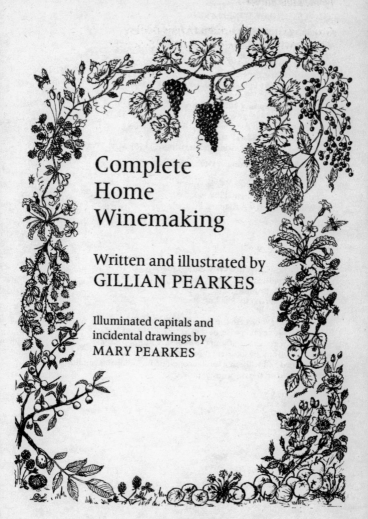

Complete
Home
Winemaking

Written and illustrated by
GILLIAN PEARKES

Illuminated capitals and
incidental drawings by
MARY PEARKES

Mandarin

A Mandarin Paperback

COMPLETE HOME WINEMAKING

First published in Great Britain 1962
by Herbert Jenkins Ltd
First paperback edition published by Methuen Paperbacks 1978
This edition published 1989
by Mandarin Paperbacks
Michelin House, 81 Fulham Road, London SW3 6RB

Mandarin is an imprint of the Octopus Publishing Group

British Library Cataloguing in Publication Data

Pearkes, Gillian
    Complete home winemaking. – 3rd ed.
    1. Wines. Making – Amateurs' manuals
    I. Title
    641.8'72

ISBN 0-7493-0029-9

Photoset by Rowland Phototypesetting Ltd
Bury St Edmunds, Suffolk
Printed in Great Britain
by Cox and Wyman Ltd, Reading, Berks

Contents

List of Diagrams		*page* 7
Introduction		9
1.	Equipment Needed	11
2.	Winemaking	15
3.	The Winemaker's Garden	32
4.	Fruit Wines	53
5.	Flower Wines	58
6.	Silver Birch Sap Wine	62
7.	The Winemaker's Vineyard	64
8.	Grape Winemaking	87
9.	Cider and Perry	95
10.	Liqueur Making	107
Appendix 1: Weights and Measures Conversion Table		115
Appendix 2: List of Suppliers		116
Bibliography		119
Index		121

Diagrams

1. Planting, training and pruning apple trees 38
2. A new method of training half standard apple trees 41
3. Fan trained fruit trees 42
4. Protecting your fruit trees 43
5. Espalier trained fruit trees 44
6. Cordon trained fruit trees 44
7. Training blackcurrant bushes 48
8. Training gooseberry bushes 49
9. Training blackberry, loganberry, tayberry etc. 49
10. Training raspberry bushes 50
11. The Winemaker's Garden 52
12. Training grape vines 69

This book is dedicated
to my mother

Introduction

ather than following the format of all other books on home winemaking which tend to be weak on technique and present the reader with endless pages of repetitive recipes, I have concentrated upon advising in great depth on the process of making wine from a variety of bases — fruit in the main — that will make really delicious well balanced wines. I have avoided the way-out raw materials which create end products that are at best unpalatable, at worst lethal potions destined for the poor unsuspecting drainage system at a very early stage.

With the increasing concern by the consumer today with the level of chemicals in food and drink, the trend towards searching for antibiotic and growth promoter free meat, and organically grown fruit and vegetables, I strongly emphasise that the winemaker should consider the benefits of using space in his or her garden, even the walls and fences if nothing else, for producing fruit for winemaking. Fruit bushes and canes will begin bearing an excellent crop in their second year, and fruit trees will start yielding in their third year. Thereafter you will have a free and increasing supply of fresh, clean beautiful fruit both for the table and for winemaking.

A word of caution here. Though it may cost a little more initially to go to a really good nursery for your fruit plants, you will never regret doing so, for they produce strong healthy plants, bushes and trees which will take well, grow well and crop well. Plants purchased from cheap weekend newspaper advertisements and glossy catalogue offers are often imported from the Far East, often have poor roots, incorrect root stocks and maybe a virus which will inhibit growth, yield and quality for the life of the plant. Inferior stock = inferior fruit. A good nursery takes pride in, and stakes its reputation on, selling good, viable, true to name plants that will be an advertisement for them forever. A good plant costs no more to care for thereafter.

A section of the book is devoted to the winemaker's garden, where suggestions are made on how one may produce enough fruit from the smallest garden for the annual wine requirement, with guidelines on choice of varieties for flavour, on planting, training, pruning and a high level of production; followed by a section on planting vines for grape production, for grape wines are obviously hard to beat.

Apples are second only to grapes as a base for home wine-making, used either alone for white wines, or for cider. So apple tree planting and training are covered comprehensively in diagram form, and the production of apple wine and cider making are covered in depth.

A book is useless to the reader without a comprehensive section on sources of supply for everything he or she might need; many books fail here leaving the poor reader in a highly enthusiastic state, aching to begin but with no means of acquiring any of the necessary materials and equipment.

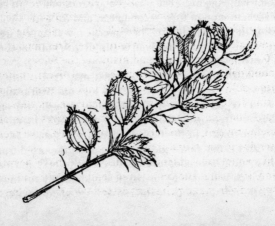

1. *Equipment Needed*

he equipment you use for your wine-making can be as simple or as sophisticated as you like; obviously the choice will depend on your annual volume of production and be geared to the degree of expenditure and expertise you wish to bring to bear on your winemaking effort.

Country wines have been made for centuries in the United Kingdom from all the garden and hedgerow fruits as they come into season throughout the summer and autumn. The country housewife considered her wines a natural part of her life, alongside the jams and jellies, the bread making, the cooking and preserving of meat, fruit and vegetables, also often beer and liqueur making. The wines were for drinking with meals, for producing when visitors called and also for helping to ward off or fight colds and influenza, sore throats and certain other ills and as a warming and reviving influence in periods of intense cold.

The housewife of earlier centuries had a very limited selection of basic equipment available for her winemaking. She would have had large earthenware bowls for steeping the fruit for flavour extraction, and earthenware jars of sizes ranging from 4 to 30 litres for fermenting and maturing the wines. For larger amounts oaken casks would have been used. In early times these wines would not have been bottled as they are today but racked off (transferred) into many small earthenware jars and served as needed from these. Jugs in a wide range of sizes from about 5 litres downwards, again in earthenware, would have been used for serving to guests and at the table.

The white and lighter red wines would have been drunk young, soon after the cessation of fermentation, and only the strong red wines and rich sweet dessert wines would have been stored away to mature and improve for many months, even years.

These lovely winemaking vessels of the past are now collectors pieces and are expensive to buy; as recently as only ten to fifteen years ago they sold for mere pence. Many wine merchants, cider makers and breweries sold their wares in these jars – most are printed or incised with the name or logo of the establishment whence they originated. Presumably the customer returned to the wine shop or brewery and had his jars refilled as necessary. Once these concerns turned over to bottling their entire output, these containers would have become obsolete.

For the winemaker, earthenware vessels have both good and bad points. They provide an ideal environment in that the wines are stored in the cool and dark – dark being essential for red wines which can be severely bleached by exposure to light; indeed light is considered injurious to Champagne and other sparkling wines. The bad point is that one cannot see if one has managed to achieve total cleanliness inside – any mould or residue could contaminate and ruin a new wine. A handful of fine gravel, some sand, piping hot water and a dash of bleach shaken around vigorously for some five minutes or so would eliminate these problems in all but the most stubborn of cases – but still one cannot see inside as one can with glass jars to check if they really are totally clean.

The glass Winchester and demijohn jars are the basis of the country winemaker's equipment today. They are cheap, easy to check for cleanliness, and stack neatly on shelves. They are also light to carry. Glass carboys, in sizes from 13·5 to 45 litres in capacity, are imported from Italy protected by a basket made of plastic and are excellent vessels for the home winemaker. They have handles at either side which help one in coping with the greater weights involved.

The risk of breakage with glass is always a problem. To-morrow's vessels are of polyethylene – proper wine tanks made by a vast German firm, which has the foresight to make sizes right down to 50 litres alongside the large sizes for commercial winemakers. These have a carrying handle at each side, a tap, and a large air-tight screw-on lid, complete with air lock, to facilitate cleaning and filling. The ideal vessel.

The pressure barrel has of course revolutionised home beer making, enabling a highly professional end product to be made, and joy of joys, allowing the beer to be drawn off and the remainder kept 100 per cent sound by virtue of the CO_2 pressure valve. The CO_2 replaces the diminishing beer right down to the last drop, preventing oxidation and spoilage and keeping the beer fresh and sparkling. With great care and attention to detail these barrels should enable us to tackle sparkling wine production – an exciting prospect.

We have therefore developed from early times when people used goatskins, then amphorae which evolved into earthenware jars, then oak and chestnut casks, next glass and now polythene. I expect that today's trend back towards the ways of yesterday and organic fruit and vegetable production will create a revival of demand for the beautiful earthenware jars of the past, which may still be found at sale rooms and in antique shops in country areas.

I have a lovely collection of earthenware jars and have made a real effort to obtain those stamped with names of wine and cider makers and brewers of Devon, Dorset and Somerset – my area of the country. They are beautiful, timeless and a great joy.

Other equipment

The polythene bucket and tub have replaced the earthenware steeping containers of the past. A fine mesh sieve will be needed, with either a polythene or stainless steel mesh. Two or three sizes of plastic funnel are useful, as also are graduated plastic jugs. With the addition of one or two very long-handled wooden spoons one is equipped for basic wine production. Items such as a syphon tube (or Colley pump) are vital for racking from one vessel to another.

The more ambitious winemaker will need a fruit crusher and a small or medium-sized wine press to extract the juice from the fruit, particularly if the production of cider from apples and wine from grapes are being contemplated. Often several winemakers group together to share the cost of these larger items. Lastly, a weighing machine is handy.

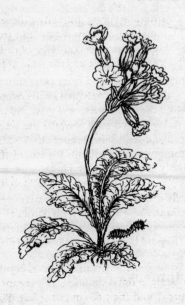

2. *Winemaking*

Juice extraction

There are four distinctly different methods of making country wines, and the method you choose will be ruled by both the amount of fruit available and the scale of the operation.

1 Hot Steeping. For the winemaker who is happy to make the odd few litres of wine, steeping the fruit in boiling water is the easiest approach. Firstly, be sure that your fruit is clean, fresh and sound, no rotten or unripe fruit should be included. Wash if necessary.

You will require some 2 to 3·5 kilogrammes of fruit per 5 litres, which should be placed in your polythene fermenter tub. If you are using solely soft fruit, such as gooseberries, raspberries, blackcurrants or similar, either individually or mixed, just pour on 2·5 litres of boiling water per 5 litres of proposed wine. Cover with fine muslin, then a blanket and leave to cool.

Add some wine yeast when the liquid is comfortable to the touch, innoculating at the recommended dose for the volume of wine being made, and then re-cover the vat. Place in a warm situation.

After some twelve to thirty-six hours in a warm room, fermentation should begin. This will be made evident by frothing or a rim of bubbles around the edge of the liquid. A gentle crackling sound can be heard when the ferment has become fully active.

2 Cool Steeping. A widely practised method is to soak the fruit in warm or cold water, with some yeast added, in a warm room for several days. This allows the natural enzymes present in the fruit to act upon the skins and break them down. The containers must be kept carefully closed during this process to keep out any bacteria or insects. An enzyme can be purchased, such as Pectozyme, which will enhance and speed up this process. Then continue as in 1 above.

3 Boiling. This is an alternative method whereby the fruit is boiled to sterilise it, then cooled before adding a wine yeast and steeping as usual. This method is not recommended except in extreme cases, as the natural fruit enzymes are all destroyed and, in most cases, the result is a hazy wine that refuses to clear.

4 Pressing. With soft fruits, or those that can be pulped such as apples and pears, this is the best method as it extracts the juice with a minimum amount of solids, whereas the former method is best for stoned fruit. Ideally, a proper fruit press should be bought, borrowed, or made for this purpose. The fruit should be pulped first. In the case of soft fruit this is to ensure that the juice is extracted from every berry, for even with many tons of pressure from above, an unbroken berry will be supported by those surrounding it and will not burst. Harder fruits such as apples and pears must be broken up before any juice extraction can take place at all. Pulping can be carried out either by use of a proper fruit crusher, or by a more basic method. For soft fruit treading is the traditional process by which the skins are broken, and it is surprisingly efficient. Otherwise a small half-cask, which has had its bottom filled in so that it stands flat on the floor, can be utilised. Place some fruit in this and just pound it with a blunt instrument such as a hardwood fencing stake. This will even work with apples and pears – after the first few are pulped this holds the fruit steady and it becomes easier.

After washing the press, line the basket with a sheet of nylon curtain netting simply draped inside – this is to contain pieces of skin and pips and, in the case of very soft fruit, to prevent the pulp from squeezing out between the slats of the basket. Then tip in the pulped fruit and do make sure that the surface of the pulp is level before putting the pressure plate on top and commencing pressing. If it is not level the press can be damaged as pressure is applied unevenly. Do not forget to have a clean bucket beneath the lip to collect the juice as it flows out, and to have a second bucket close at hand with which to replace it when it is full. Pour the juice into a clean, sterilised container.

When you apply pressure to the wine press, do not strain yourself. When the going gets hard, simply leave it for a while and let the juice drip out slowly. As this occurs, the pressure will be gradually relaxed and shortly you will be able to apply some more pressure with comparative ease. Keep going until the flow of juice really becomes meagre – this is the time to unpack the press.

When all the juice has been extracted, the cake of dry fruit pulp can be removed and placed on your compost heap. Apple and grape pulp can be fed to cattle, sheep, pigs or horses.

The juice should be sulphited (i.e. have wine sulphur added) at the rate of 5 grammes per 100 litres and left to settle for about twenty-four hours. This allows most of the solids to drop to the bottom. The juice can now be syphoned off the sediment into a clean sterile container with the correct amount of sugar already poured in, and be innoculated with yeast and, if necessary, a yeast nutrient. Then continue as for 1 above.

Yeast

Yeast, when allowed to multiply in a fruit juice to make an alcoholic drink, converts the natural and added sugars into alcohol and carbon dioxide which rises up through the wine in the form of bubbles.

Few people rely entirely upon the natural yeast which exists on the leaves and fruit of all plants. See under 'Wild Yeast' below.

I wholeheartedly recommend the German wine yeast SIHA; this yeast has such excellent properties and capabilities. We professional winegrowers seldom use anything else after once trying it.

Developed by an eminent German professor of microbiology in Darmstadt, through years of patient study and selection of the major active cells of this particular strain, this yeast comes in granular form in half-kilogramme vacuum packs. No yeast starter is needed – this in itself saves a great deal of time and uncertainty – just sprinkle a little yeast directly on to the surface of the must (unfermented juice). Fermentation should begin within three days, usually in a matter of a few hours. The action will be gentle and steady, which will help to enhance and retain the full bouquet and flavour of the fruit, the whole process taking weeks rather than days.

Should a wild eruptive ferment occur, this is because the wild yeast cells were not all destroyed by the initial addition of wine sulphur. Wine sulphur inhibits the growth of wild yeasts, whereas wine yeasts can survive in the presence of a stronger dose of this chemical. This can make a ghastly mess as the vessels overflow with seemingly endless amounts of foam. If you can find a length of polythene tube of the same diameter as the hole in the bung closing your vessel, the fermentation lock (which prevents air access to your wine) can be removed and replaced by the tube, which is then led into a bucket beneath a few centimetres of sulphur solution. This will then trap the froth. The wild yeast dies when 4 per cent of alcohol is achieved.

As time passes the yeast cells will die and settle out to form a firm, shallow sediment on the base of the fermentation vessel. This enables you to syphon off the wine right down to the yeast with virtually no loss of volume. Many yeasts form a deep flocculating layer of detritus which it is impossible to prevent from being sucked up by the syphon tube during racking. Another plus factor for this SIHA yeast.

One final point. SIHA yeast will continue fermenting at extremely low temperatures, as low as 5°C (40°F). Cool temperature fermentation is not a process usually adopted by country winemakers, who tend to keep their wines in a hot room until the cessation of the primary fermentation. However, once started, if one conducts the first ferment at 8°C–10°C (45°F–50°F), the slow gentle activity will prevent the more delicate and subtle flavours and bouquets being 'boiled' away by a more vigorous fermentation. Wines that have experienced a slow cool fermentation are far superior to those produced from a fast hot ferment.

Once the fermentation has really started, the fruit pulp will begin to rise to the surface. This must be pushed down, broken up and, if possible, turned over at least twice per day. If this is not carried out the fruit and skins on the top begin to acetify and your beautiful wine will be turned to vinegar and sour water.

White wines

Leave white wines for four days fermenting on the skins and pulp. Sterilise your fermentation jar or vessel, then place your large nylon sieve over a clean bucket or bowl (or a funnel inserted into the neck of a fermentation jar, in which case put the sugar in first) and strain the pulp; use a wooden or plastic spoon to stir and push the pulp through the sieve.

For every 4·5 litres of wine you should add 1 kilogramme of cane sugar to the must. This is poured into the fermentation vessel along with the wine, the juice of two lemons and sufficient yeast nutrient for the volume of wine being made (instructions for whichever particular brand you use will be on the packet). The pouring of the wine on to the sugar will bring about a revival of vigorous activity, so therefore it is necessary *not* to fill the vessel completely at this stage, otherwise excessive frothing will cause the wine to overflow with subsequent loss of volume and mess to be cleared up. As this turbulence gradually dies down the winemaker can then top up the vessel with any extra wine, or with water. Fit a tight cork or lid to this vessel and insert a fermentation lock.

Fermentation lock

The fermentation or air lock is a simple device that allows the carbon dioxide gas to escape but excludes the entry of any air, bacteria and insects into the wine. You half fill it with a 2 per cent sulphur solution so that there is a sterile seal between the wine and the atmosphere. At a pinch, a piece of polythene tubing can be used as a makeshift alternative, but it must fit tightly into the hole in the top of the bung or lid. Simply let the loose end hang in a jar of sulphur solution and watch the gas bubble out.

Red wines

Leave red wines to ferment for seven days on their pulp, for you are extracting colour here as well as flavour. Seven days, no more and no less, for if left longer the colour begins to fade. Thereafter continue as advised for white wines above – but remember to ferment, store and bottle your red wines in opaque vessels: brown glass or earthenware jars, or if polythene containers are used these should be covered with some light-proof material; finally put the wine into green bottles.

Once the initial fermentation has ceased, test your wine with a hydrometer floating in a trial glass filled with the wine. This test will indicate if there is any sugar left to ferment in the wine – sugar is registered as specific gravity, as density, as matter, and the hydrometer – which is simply a weighted float – will show a reading of 1000 (o) or below on the scale if all the sugar has been converted to alcohol and carbon dioxide, whereas if there is still some sugar present in the wine the hydrometer will float higher and register a number such as 1020, 1015 or 1010 – in which case pour the wine sample back into the vessel, replace the cover and the air lock and test it again in a week or two.

Hydrometers can be purchased cheaply at Boots or any home winemaking store.

Racking

Once the wine has fermented out to dryness or near dryness, or when the activity has ceased, it is time for it to be racked. Racking is to pump or syphon the wine off the sediment which is composed of dead and dying yeast cells and precipitated fruit pulp. It left on this sediment, or lees as it is called, autolysis or auto-digestion will begin, which will taint the wine with an off flavour and smell.

Again, according to the volume of wine to be dealt with, the winemaker will have either a length of polythene tubing or one of the proprietary syphon pumps (or even a small electrically-driven pump can be used provided it is made from a corrosion resistant material). However, with the simple tube, one end is placed in the wine and the other is placed in your mouth. Then you suck until you taste the wine, swiftly place a finger over the end of the tube and then convey this end to the clean container, remove your finger and let gravity do the rest. The only thing to remember is that you must have the receiving vessel lower than the bottom of the container you are emptying. It is difficult to describe the technique, but the winemaker soon becomes adept at guiding the suction end of the pipe down inside the full vessel, whilst at the same time gently tipping it so that every last drop of clear wine is extracted without stirring up the lees.

The German polythene tanks have a convenient tap at the base, so one simply slips a tube into or over the tap and down into the top of the receiving vessel, again gently tipping the tank as the sediment is neared so that every last drop is transferred.

Fill up the vessel with spare wine or water – this time to very near the top – and tightly re-fit the cork, bung or lid and insert an air lock. A gentle secondary fermentation may or may not occur, according to the time of year. Keep the wine in cool conditions so that a gradual clearing and maturing process will take its course. Repeat the racking operation one month later, and thereafter at two monthly intervals.

Cold stabilisation

A hard, frosty January or February is the very best aid to clearing any wines. Stand your vessels outside, but out of the wind in a fairly sheltered situation. The alcohol will prevent the wine from freezing, but the cold usually drops out all the solids and fine particles. Leave out for several nights.

Immediately the wines have cleared they must be racked off the sediment, so no fine particles are re-absorbed into the wine. Once again top up and store the wines until bottling.

Alternatively, if there is no cold snap, and your containers are small enough, ten days in the refrigerator is a fair second best.

Filtering and bottling

Before bottling, the wines should be tested for stability. Test the specific gravity with your hydrometer. A reading of below 1000 (usually abbreviated to 0) will ensure that all the sugar has been converted into alcohol. Above this figure there is the risk that the wine could re-ferment in the bottle with disastrous (to say nothing of explosive!) results. So one has either to encourage the wine to ferment out to dryness if a dry wine is desired; or if the plan is to produce a sweet wine then the fermentation is halted at this point.

Stopping a fermentation process before it comes to its natural conclusion is not very difficult but care must be taken at all stages to ensure sterile vessels and equipment are used, because any contamination is almost certain to re-activate the wine in the bottle.

Wine sulphur is not the ideal chemical for stopping a fermentation since it does not destroy bacteria and, unless the level is unacceptably high, is not certain to kill yeast cells but only inhibit their activity – probably until the weather warms up. Potassium sorbate is an alternative which does render the wine sterile, but dosage must be carefully checked since using too much can leave a strange papery taste in the finished product. For most wines a dosage of 250 milligrammes per litre is recommended, unless the alcohol content is high (above 12 per cent) in which case the dose can be lowered to 200 milligrammes per litre. Dissolve the correct amount of sorbate in a small amount of water and then stir this solution into the wine. The solution does not keep, so only mix enough for each application.

Before bottling, the wine should not only be rendered inert, but clarification does improve the appearance of your wine. As mentioned above, cold stabilisation will settle out most solids and render the wine clear. If this is a crystal clarity, or you are not worried by a slight cloudiness in the wine and a sediment in the bottles, then this is fine and you can go ahead and bottle at this stage. However, to be certain of no activity in the bottle and a true bright clarity then filtration is the answer.

A Vinamat filter is a very reasonably priced piece of equipment and certainly makes the process very simple and quick. Be sure to clean and sterilise the entire filter with your sulphur solution. Depending upon the volume (and cloudiness) of the wine to be filtered you must now select the density of filter sheet that you need. If it is only a few litres, you can most likely get away with just using sterile (Steril) sheets, but for a larger amount I would advise a double filtering, using coarse (Grov) sheets first and then finishing off with the sterile pads. An alternative, if the wine is very clear and stable, is to use clear (Klar) sheets which do not sterilise but simply polish your wine. The latter are the best choice for a red wine.

I will run through a typical filtering session. After sterilising the Vinamat, select two coarse pads and fit these into the two halves of the filter body, remembering to place them in with the smooth, patterned side bearing the writing against the filter and the rough side visible. The filtration medium is bonded to a paper backing, and if you get the sheet the wrong way round, instead of filtering your wine you will simply render it more cloudy by removing the filter fibres because you have pushed the wine through backwards. Once the sheets are in place I then douse them with sulphur solution before swiftly putting the spacer ring in place and then fitting the two halves together. Put on the washers and the wing nuts and then tighten them gradually in opposing pairs; this prevents undue stress on the plastic filter. When all are tight, flushing can commence.

Connect up the pipes to the spigots protruding from the filter: the tube from the pressure vessel is fitted to the single centre pipe in the spacer ring; the bifurcated tube is affixed to the two spigots on the top and bottom of the filter body. Fill the pressure container up to the mark with clean water, screw on the pump unit and apply pressure. After a few gurgles the water will fill the filter and begin to pour out of the tube (remember to have this dangling into a sink or bucket). As the flow slackens, keep on pumping up the pressure and continue until 4 or 5 centimetres remain. Now taste the water coming out of the tube. If it tastes of paper another 4 or 5 litres of clean water will have to be flushed through. Continue this process until the paper taste has vanished – sometimes 4 or 5 litres will suffice; with another batch of filter pads you may need 12 litres to fully flush them.

Before the wine is put in just tip out any water remaining in the vessel. Now stick a funnel in the top and gently pour in the wine, which should have been sulphured to a level of 35–50 milligrammes per litre, the stronger dose used if the wine is very cloudy. Only fill to the mark on the container and then put on the pump. When pressure is applied the first of the wine is obviously going to mix with the water still in the filter, so keep on tasting the filtrate and let it run away until there is more wine than water. Now let the filtrate run into a jar or container – remember to have enough cleaned to take the volume of wine you are handling. When the vessel is almost empty, gently unscrew the pump so that the sheets are not flexed by a sudden decrease in pressure; refill with more wine and continue until all is filtered, or until the pumping becomes difficult and the flow is minimal. Should this latter occur, then the sheets are clogged and must be changed and the new ones flushed.

The final filtering is undertaken with sterile (or possibly clear in the case of a red wine) sheets. Prepare as above, but this time, when the wine/water mixture becomes more wine than water, catch the first half litre/litre in a jug, to be returned to the bulk, before starting to fill the bottles – this ensures that all bottles will contain full strength wine. Bottles should be corked as soon as the bubbles subside, this sometimes can take as much as ten minutes.

When filtering is over, take down the filter and clean throughout with a chlorine solution, then rinse very well before storing in a cupboard away from dust.

Regarding bottling, choice of bottles is important: it creates a good impression if you select the correct style of bottle to suit your wine. For the drier white wines a Hock or Mosel bottle should be used; for the sweet whites the same design can be utilised or you could store it in clear, white Bordeaux (Sauternes) bottles. For red wines a green Bordeaux or Burgundy style is ideal.

Bottles, if they have been used before, must be washed carefully with a weak chlorine/soda solution (Chempro SDP is extremely good) and a bottle brush. Hold the bottle up to the light to make certain that there are no spots or smears inside – these will probably be bacteria. If the marks are so stubborn that they will not budge, discard that bottle – it is not worth risking your precious wine in such a container. Rinse well three times with fresh water to remove all traces of cleansing agent.

All bottles must be sterilised with the 2 per cent sulphur solution, even those you have just washed. Then let them drain upside down for a while before filling – this allows the interior to dry out and will not dilute the wine at all.

Selection of corks is of paramount importance – they are the only thing that is between your wine and the damaging effects of the air, so it is vital to buy good corks. You should obtain them from a reputable cork merchant rather than relying upon those available in the high street. He can even supply them waxed and pre-sterilised which speeds up the process of bottling. I cannot stress this enough: poor corks which are either too thin, too hard or porous are the cause of probably 75 per cent of problems. I have seen bottles which have leaked half their contents on to the floor due to poor corks, and of course the remainder is rendered undrinkable through contact with the air.

Unwaxed and unsterilised corks must be washed and sterilised. Soak them for a couple of hours in a 1·5 per cent sulphur solution and then rinse twice, shaking them about vigorously, in clean water. This will remove any dust from the corks which would otherwise get into your wine. It makes this cleaning process easier if you have a muslin bag to contain the corks. The wet corks should now be permitted to dry before use or else you will get a drop of sulphury water squeezed from each cork as it is forced into the bottle neck which firstly corrodes the corker, and then drips into the wine, carrying with it the dissolved metal in a black smudge that it has picked up from the corker.

Corks should be driven home to within 6 millimetres of the surface of the wine, leaving a minimal ullage or air gap. Bottles should be filled with this in mind, so make a mental note of the depth of your corks and fill the bottles, by eye, correspondingly.

A capsule or foil is not essential, but it does give a nice finish to a bottle. They are available in either shrink on form or in metal, which needs a tool or machine to create a smooth finish.

Labels can be purchased at all home winemaking shops, but why not be original and design your own, or have an artistic friend do one for you? They can be very reasonably copied at one of the myriad high street duplicating establishments and are easily affixed with heavy-duty wallpaper paste.

Storage of bottled wine should ideally be in the dark and in a stable temperature of about 45–52 °F. There are various methods for binning, or stacking, the bottles, or simple racks can be made or purchased – one of the most basic just consists of a stack of tile land drains. We bin our bottles on a level bed of sand some 5 centimetres deep, side by side and shoulder to shoulder so they interlock in stacks two deep and rising about seventeen high.

Cleaning and sterilising

One vital practice that all winemakers must fiercely adopt is to sterilise every piece of equipment before use. There are two chemicals that one can use here: chlorine and sulphur. For dirty jars and buckets, and for fermentation vessels as soon as they are emptied of wine, one can use a mild solution of chlorine (domestic bleach), or alternatively buy the chemical in powdered form such as Chempro SDP which is readily dissolved in water. After using a hypochlorite solution like this remember to rinse very, *very* well with clean water to remove any traces of the chemical. Omit this precaution and you will end up with a wine that tastes of disinfectant!

It is a simple task to clean and sterilise open and large-topped vessels, but a tight-necked jar is a problem. Coarse sand and fine gravel, very hot water and a little chlorine swirled around for a while will usually shift the most stubborn stains and moulds. Do remember to rinse well – at least three times. Please, *never* use chlorine on oak.

Potassium metabisulphite (wine sulphur) can be purchased from David Cowderoy, and should be made up into a 2 per cent solution and kept in a corked jar or screw-top plastic container. Remember that it will corrode all metals other than stainless steel. This liquid can then be used as a final rinse for all equipment immediately before it is used. Jars, sieves, tubing, buckets etc. should all receive this treatment.

Caution

Never use containers or equipment in your winemaking other than those made from glass, food/wine grade polythene, stainless steel or oak. Brass, copper, iron, steel, zinc or aluminium must never come into contact with fruit juice or wine, for it will pick up minute quantities of these metals in solution and will at best taint the wine, at worst poison the drinker.

Never use chlorine for sterilising oak or anything made of wood as it will be absorbed and will taint and ruin your wine. Sulphur is fine for use with wood.

Wild yeast

Wild yeast cells are present on all fruit and used to be relied on for much home winemaking in the past. Apparently a staggering 10,000 wild yeast cells are present on the skin of a grape! Alongside these wild yeast cells are also thousands of bacteria cells, all waiting to spoil your wines if given the chance.

The problem with wild yeasts is that they die when an alcohol content of about 4 per cent by volume has been reached, and wine with such a low alcohol level will be vulnerable to attack by every form of bacteria and disease that was on the fruit at the time of harvest. The wine simply will not keep, for 4 per cent is no preservative for a wine – an alcohol level of 10·0–10·5 per cent is really needed by white wines, and up to 12·0–12·5 per cent by volume is required by red wines.

So today we eliminate the wild yeast with an addition of wine sulphur (potassium metabisulphite) at the rate of 5 grammes (1 level teaspoon) per 100 litres (22 gallons) of must for a clean fresh fruit with no mould or rot present, and at 10 grammes (1 heaped teaspoon) per 100 litres for fruit with some mouldiness, or that is not quite fresh. Make it your principle, if possible, not to use damaged or mouldy fruit. Mix the sulphur in very well for it has a tendency to stay stratified in a layer some two-thirds of the way up from the bottom of the must.

After twenty-four hours the sulphur will have mostly dissipated into the atmosphere, and you can add your cane sugar; Tate and Lyle is recommended here for it contains no additions that can cause a stubborn residual starch or protein haze in the finished wine, which can result from the use of other sugars, especially beet sugar.

Stuck fermentation

Sometimes the fermentation refuses to start, or unaccountably stops at some stage before the sugar has been fully converted to alcohol. This can be due to a variety of causes.

Remedies. Should your fermentation refuse to begin, this can be due to the temperature being too low for the yeast to function; or the level of sulphur in the juice could be so great that it kills or inhibits the action of the yeast; the addition of too much sugar owing to a miscalculation of amounts; the acidity of the juice could be too high to permit the process to start; or possibly the wine yeast is too old and has ceased to be potent.

Low Temperature. Most wine yeasts will not multiply at a temperature lower than 15°C (60°F) so that the answer here is either to move the vessels concerned into a warmer situation, or raise the temperature of the liquid by dropping in an immersion heater or surrounding the container with one or two heating elements of some type (i.e. Brewbelts). However, the new German SIHA yeast will start and conduct a fermentation at a temperature as low as 8°C (45°F).

Sulphur Level. The remedy here is basically to leave the must for a further period until the sulphur level has dropped sufficiently for the fermentation to commence. Another twenty-four hours should suffice in all but the worst cases. The higher the amount of solids in the must, the quicker the drop in sulphur content.

Too Sweet. Fermentation can be inhibited if the winemaker, by mistake, adds the yeast before adding the sugar: the sugar can therefore form a dense impenetrable layer over the yeast granules and deprive the yeast of the essential oxygen it requires to begin multiplying. The remedy is to pour or pump the juice into a new vessel once or, ideally, twice to allow the sugar to dissolve into the whole volume of the juice, and then re-yeast the must.

Too Acid. Buy a kilogramme of Acidex from your wine chemical store. Too high an acidity can inhibit the start of fermentation – a juice created from unripe apples, grapes or other fruit can cause this problem. The cure here is to lower the acidity to an acceptable level so that the yeast can begin working.

The use of Acidex is quite straightforward. By finding the initial acidity on the appropriate set of tables (and do not forget that they refer to a bulk of 1,000 litres) and cross-referencing this with the desired level of acid, you will find there two numbers. One will tell you the amount of Acidex needed for the process of reducing the level of acid in 1,000 litres. The other gives you the number of litres upon which the chemical action must take place (you never reduce the acid level on the entire bulk of the must or wine, only a percentage), once again this figure is the amount for treating 1,000 litres. It is simple arithmetic to work out the ratio for your amount of must or wine. You then add the Acidex to 10 per cent of the amount to be treated and stir or shake well. Over some ten minutes you should then add the remaining 90 per cent, stirring all the while. Leave the treated liquid to settle for some eight to twelve hours and then carefully rack off from the thick white sediment, returning the de-acidified fluid to the bulk of the wine or must.

The result of lowering the acidity is dramatic in a wine must, for it will now begin to ferment almost immediately it is re-innoculated with yeast. Any level of acidity above 12 (expressed as tartaric) should be lowered to a starting level of 10. The process of fermentation will lower this to 6·0–6·5, which is the correct level for a white wine ready for bottling.

Old Yeast. Simply innoculate with a fresh culture of yeast.

Re-starting a stuck fermentation

This is a task that requires patience. Clean and sterilise a fresh container of the same size (or slightly larger if possible) as that containing the stopped ferment. Into this vessel introduce some lees from a new wine that has just been racked for the first or second time – failing this some of the lees from under any young wine that is in bulk.

> use ½ litre for a 5 litre jar
> use 1 litre for a 20 litre jar
> use 2 litres for a 45 litre jar, and so on pro rata

Now add the same amount of your stuck wine. Once this is seen to be actively fermenting, add a second such amount and await signs of activity. Carry on adding a little at a time until all of the stopped wine has been added (or the container filled). It should now ferment out to dryness without further problems. NEVER add the lees to the bulk of the stopped wine, always add the wine to the yeast, and in small quantities – this is the secret of success.

Wine chemical store

A winemaker should have a store cupboard containing all the chemicals likely to be needed for the process, including:

Potassium Metabisulphite	2 kg	for stabilising wine and sterilising equipment
Acidex	1 kg	for reduction of acidity in wine

Potassium Sorbate	1 kg	for killing bacteria and yeast, and to achieve stability in some difficult wines
Charcoal	1 kg	for removal of excess colour and bad odours from white wine
Citric Acid	1 kg	for increasing acidity in flat, low acid wines

Essential equipment

Hydrometer and Trial Jar	for testing specific gravity of juices and wines
Funnels	one or two sizes in plastic
Nylon Sieve	for straining juices
Measuring Jars	once again various sizes in plastic
Plastic Bowl	for mixing, steeping etc.
Cleaning Brushes	for inside jars, vessels and bottles
Fermenting Tub	polythene container with a good lid
Polythene Tubing	for racking etc.

Useful equipment

Acid Testing Kit	for ascertaining acid levels in juices and wines
Sulphur Test Kit	for testing sulphur levels in wine; most useful at bottling
Vinometer	useful for finding alcohol content of wine
Small Weighing Machine	very useful for measuring chemicals etc.
Fruit Crusher	to prepare fruit for pressing
Wine Press	for ideal juice extraction
Vinamat Filter	ideal for achieving stability and that final clear polish to your wine

3. *The Winemaker's Garden*

f your garden is small, then a relatively small area need be put aside to create the winemaker's garden – obviously the larger the garden and the greater your annual wine production, the larger the area which may be devoted to planting and cropping fruit bushes, canes and trees. Most gardens have walls or fences, all of which can be used to train plants against, for wall grown plants crop more heavily given the added protection and warmth thus afforded.

Warning

The price difference between really well-grown, healthy, well-rooted plants and the slightly cheaper fruit plants from less than reputable firms is relatively narrow, but the performance of the plants from a good nursery is so vastly superior that one should never be tempted by the lesser sources of supply. Once planted, good plants cost no more to feed, train and spray than their cheaper, lesser contemporaries, so always go to a good firm for true-to-name, well-rooted and virus-free stock.

Range

Fruit forms the best base of any material for the aspiring home winemaker, and the choice of fruit plants today is so wide and so interesting that once planted and cropping you could be spoilt for choice. If you are a winemaker who opts for making 5 or 10 litres of a very wide range of types and tastes, then you do not need many plants of each type; for example raspberries, blackcurrants etc. If, on the other hand, you like making 40, 80 or more litres of each type of wine, then obviously you need a small plot of each type of fruit to provide sufficient raw materials.

There is also the satisfaction of knowing that you have complete control over the health and well-being of the fruit you produce; you can choose the nutrition and decide on the sprays respectively to feed and care for your plants, and you can therefore be sure that no harmful or poisonous substances are used which might taint the wine or upset the drinker.

Planning

Have a look at the plan on page 52 – which is only a suggestion for every garden is different – either to reorganise totally your existing garden with home production in mind, or simply to adapt and utilise areas in your garden which might at present be producing nothing. Once dug, planted and, if necessary, supported, most of the major input effort is over, thereafter the hoe for keeping down the weeds (or a small rotavator if you have the area to merit one), the work of winter pruning, spring feeding and mulching (mulch is a mixture of wet straw, grass, leaves etc., spread on the ground to protect plants and retain moisture), spraying and the business of cropping, gathering and processing, all become so worthwhile when you experience the delight of harvesting a highly productive garden.

Rootstocks

Tree fruit plants like apples, plums and pears are grafted on to a range of differing rootstocks, each designed for a different type of location. For small, confined spaces a dwarfing rootstock is required which will control the vigour of the tree to keep it to a manageable height; whereas if you have an enormous garden or are considering planting a field or orchard, then obviously a more expansive stronger rootstock is needed to encourage the trees in question to grow larger. There are ultra dwarfing rootstocks available that enable a grower to plant trees in large tubs, and others suited to small, medium or large gardens.

Two points that must be made here are that a dwarfing rootstock encourages early cropping, but also in the long term the tree enjoys a shorter life span; whereas those trees grafted on to stronger rootstocks come into full bearing later, but live far longer before declining. Ask the nurseryman for advice on rootstocks for your situation and needs. A guide will be given later on the description of fruit tree and bush varieties, but such is the advance of horticultural technology today that new rootstocks and varieties are being produced that may, before long, supercede any advice given herein.

Apple Rootstocks

Dwarfing	M9	for small garden	space 2·5–3 metres apart
Dwarfing	M26	slightly more vigorous	space 3–4·5 metres apart
Semi-dwarfing	M7 and MM106	moderate vigour	space 3·5–5·5 metres apart
Vigorous	M2 and MM111	for poor soils	space 4·5–6 metres apart

Apples

Apples are the one fruit you should produce if you grow nothing else, for the apple is so adaptable and can be used for making wines of many types and of course for cider – quite apart from the supply of fruit for eating and cooking.

Apples may be grown as cordons or single stems trained obliquely against a wall or fence, or fan trained or even espalier trained. In this way they take up no room in the open garden, protruding a mere 15 to 30 centimetres from the face of the wall or fence. Alternatively, if your garden can take a feature tree or two planted in the lawn or a border, then one can choose a rootstock of medium vigour and in a few years you can have one or more specimen trees that are very beautiful to look at and provide gentle shade for you to sit beneath in the heat of summer.

You can purchase apple trees, and indeed pear, plum, cherry and other fruit trees, of a few years of age that have been initiated into cordons, espaliers or fans by the nursery. These will obviously be more expensive than maiden trees with just one year's growth since being grafted – maidens have a single stem of from 90 to 120 centimetres in height and you have to be prepared and confident to take over their training and future development. With the help of figures 1 to 6 you should be able to persuade your trees to adopt and follow any shape you wish. Training and pruning are an art form, a delicate and ancient craft; every cut you make is highly significant to the future form of your fruit trees and bushes.

For winemaking there are several varieties of apple that stand out above all the others, so do not be tempted to go and buy 'a few apple trees'. The names are extremely important, as the quality and performance differ widely between varieties.

Cox's Orange Pippin is an apple with a glorious flavour, both for winemaking and eating. *James Grieve* is another dual purpose variety. If you have room for a third, buy a *Bramley Seedling* for the input of acidity to your blend; it also is the very best cooking apple and keeps very well once picked. If you have the space to plant more trees, *Kingston Black* and *Dabinett* are both cider apples of great quality and, although they blend admirably with each other and indeed with all other apples, they are the only true cider apple varieties that make a superb cider on their own – a single variety cider. I have listed the five best types above but if you have still more room, plant further *Cox's Orange Pippin* and *James Grieve* trees – the former a marvellous keeper throughout the winter into spring, whereas the latter quickly passes its best and is one recommended to be consumed or used within a month or so of harvesting. Please also refer to the advice on varieties given in the chapter on cider production.

Pollination

Certain varieties of apple, and other fruit, are not fertile on their own pollen, in other words they need pollen from another variety to set the flowers. So one will need another variety to ensure a good crop – plant the pollinator to windward of the tree that requires the pollen.

Pollination is the most critical phase in the annual life cycle of all fruiting plants, and a successful fruit set is dependent upon favourable weather conditions during the flowering period. Especially vulnerable are those that flower very early: for example apricots. Ideal weather conditions are warmth, with temperatures above 10°C (50°F) by day and, particularly, by night; no driving rain, though gentle warm showers are by no means disastrous; and, of course, total absence of frosts.

Certain plants require that you, the grower, physically spread the pollen from flower to flower – indoor vines, Kiwi fruit, apricots and peaches are all plants that need assistance from the human hand during blossoming. The Victorian method was to use a rabbit's or hare's paw, but a soft-bristled, medium-sized, squirrel hair artist's paintbrush will do the task highly efficiently. Even a pinch or twist of cotton wool will suffice. Simply take up the yellow powdery pollen from the anthers on to your brush and then gently daub it on to the flowers of the tree that will not set with its own pollen. Keep returning to the pollinator tree to recharge your brush with viable pollen as you go along.

Nutrition

When planting fruit bushes and trees, dress the bottom of the hole dug out at planting time with a couple of handfuls of hoof and horn and mixed bonemeal and blend this well into the soil.

All fruit trees and bushes need to be fed each year, particularly if they are planted against a wall or fence, or if they are in a glasshouse. To function properly fruit-producing plants require annual applications of *sulphate of potash* (*not* muirate of potash) to ripen wood and buds by autumn and winter, also for the production of blossom and the ripening of the fruit. *Woodashes* (from a wood fire, *not* a coal or refuse fire) are an excellent source of potash and should always be kept for dressing fruit bushes and trees. *Superphospate* is needed to encourage photosynthesis – the process whereby the chlorophyl in the leaves of the plant absorbs sunlight and converts this into starch, which is in turn converted into sugar and stored in the ripening fruit.

Nitrogen should be applied sparingly, if at all – and only if necessary. On thin, poor soils, sandy or chalky soils, a dressing of well rotted strawy manure or compost may be added every two to three years. Nitrogen promotes fast, soft, sappy new growth in canes and leaf, and this is more often than not at the expense of fruit. Blackcurrants are one type of fruit that does require a light application of organic manure or compost every year – a mulch of compost or manure does help to suppress weeds for a time, and prevents the roots drying out in a drought. This applies to all bush, cane and tree fruit.

Planting – for all fruit trees

Check, before buying, that the plants have a good, healthy-looking fibrous root system. Take out a good hole, wider than the rootspan, and work a couple of handfuls of mixed hoof and horn and bonemeal into the soil at the bottom. With secateurs cut the ends of the roots cleanly away and then take care to spread them out evenly.

Shovel the soil back evenly into the hole, gently shaking the tree as you do so to allow the soil to filter down between and beneath the roots in order to prevent any air gaps remaining beneath the plant. Tread down the earth with your heel when the hole is half filled, then continue filling until all the soil has been returned. Then tread firmly around the stem again so that there is no movement from the plant.

Supports

All young fruit trees must be staked and tied so that they do not loosen in the wind. These can be special expanding tree ties, or nylon stockings which are hard to beat as they do not chafe or cut the bark and will expand as the tree grows. A warning here,

Figure 1 Apples

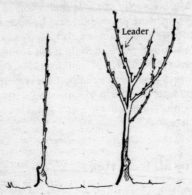

1. Newly planted maiden tree.

3. Newly planted 2 year old tree.

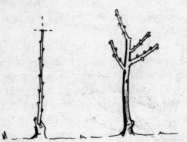

2. Maiden tree after pruning – take off top third, leave top bud facing into prevailing wind.

4. 2 year old tree after pruning – cut ⅔ off all side shoots and ½ off leader; cut to outward facing buds, and leader to bud facing west.

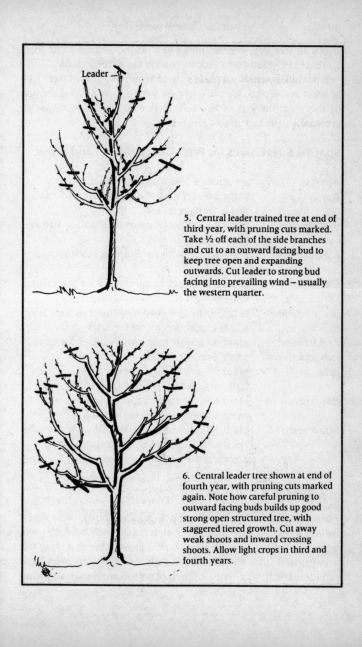

Leader

5. Central leader trained tree at end of third year, with pruning cuts marked. Take ½ off each of the side branches and cut to an outward facing bud to keep tree open and expanding outwards. Cut leader to strong bud facing into prevailing wind – usually the western quarter.

6. Central leader tree shown at end of fourth year, with pruning cuts marked again. Note how careful pruning to outward facing buds builds up good strong open structured tree, with staggered tiered growth. Cut away weak shoots and inward crossing shoots. Allow light crops in third and fourth years.

check all tree ties several times a year as the girth of some trees increases very fast and a tie can quickly cut a tree in half.

If possible keep the earth in a circle around your fruit trees free of grass and weeds, for the latter are very greedy and take much of the nutrition out of the soil. A hoe is preferable by far to weedkiller, the lazy man's method.

Spacing Suggestions for Fruit Canes, Bushes and Trees

Apples	see above – also in cider chapter
Apricots	plant 2·5–3·5 metres apart on South-facing walls, well protected
Blackberries	plant 2–2·5 metres apart on a wall or strong high trellis
Blackcurrants	plant stools 1–2 metres apart, manure and feed well
Cherries	plant 2·5–3 metres apart – can be fan trained on walls
Gooseberries	plant bushes 90–120 centimetres apart. Try and find standards 1 metre high
Peaches and Nectarines	plant on South-facing walls 2·5–3·5 metres apart. Feed very well
Plums	plant dwarf trees 2 metres apart, half-standards 3–3·5 metres apart
Raspberries	plant 60 centimetres apart, rows 1–1·5 metres apart for access into block
Strawberries	plant 38 centimetres apart in double rows, 38 centimetres apart, leave 60 centimetres between the double rows for access

Apricot

For outdoor culture plant *Moorpark*. Apricots flower very early, in late March–early April when it is usually too cold and wet outside for pollination to take place. I grow mine in a large tub and bring it into my glasshouse to blossom under cover, and pollinate the flowers with a pinch of cotton wool each day until

Figure 2 A new method of training half standard apple trees

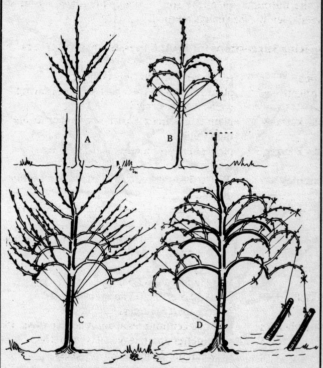

A is a 2 year specimen and has its lower branches pulled down and tied to the stem, B. This arching of the branches encourages earlier fruiting and also helps those trees with a naturally upright habit to a more open shape. Tree C at the end of the second year shows the growth made; one can continue to pull the outer branches down just one more year – D.

Figure 3 Fan Trained Fruit Trees

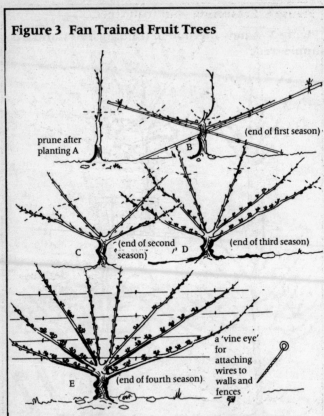

prune after planting A

(end of first season) B

(end of second season) C

(end of third season) D

(end of fourth season) E

a 'vine eye' for attaching wires to walls and fences

Stages in the development of a fan trained fruit tree, suitable for apples, pears, plums, cherries, peaches, apricots, etc. Do not expect more than two new fruiting arms each year. By the end of the fourth year you will have a fully grown tree. Prune shoots from fruiting spurs back each winter.

Figure 4 Protecting your fruit trees

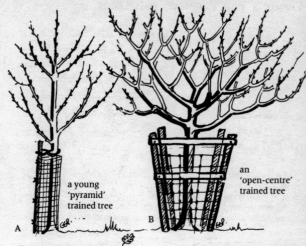

a young 'pyramid' trained tree

an 'open-centre' trained tree

A.

B.

A. All trees must be staked to keep them straight and firm, and if planted in a field be protected from rabbits and sheep with a wire netting sleeve. Tie netting to stake and let into ground at base.

B. If trees are planted in a field where horses and cattle might graze, make a strong surround fence with stakes and rails, covered with sheep or pig netting.

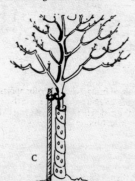

C.

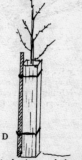

D.

C. A wrap-around tough plastic rabbit guard – good value.

D. A plastic tree shelter which brings on young whips very fast.

Figure 5 Espalier trained fruit trees

Do not attempt to produce more than two new arms each year.
Provide good support for the arms on the wall with vine eyes and
horizontal wires. Can also be grown in the open if a good enough total
support system is provided. Prune spurs back to 3 or 4 buds each
winter for apples, pears etc. Prune plums, cherries etc. in April.

Figure 6 Cordon trained fruit trees

(before pruning)

A suitable system for apples, pears, either trained on walls or fences, or on a
firm, well supported trellis in the open. Choose a dwarfing rootstock and tie
in firmly during the first few years at the desired angle, loosening the ties
each season. Note tree on the extreme right *before* winter pruning. Cut the
spurs back to leave 3 or 4 buds, from which 2 are kept to grow away and
produce fruit.

all the blooms appear set. After flowering I take the tree out again and grow it on against a warm South-facing wall. If any pruning is necessary, follow the instructions given for the peach.

Blackberries

One can buy thornless blackberries nowadays – this is a great advantage when training, cropping and winter pruning. These plants are best fan-trained on a wall, fence or trellis. After planting prune back close to the ground and allow ten, twelve or fourteen shoots to grow, which must be tied in. These canes can bear fruit in the following year. During winter pruning cut out all the canes that have borne fruit and then tie in ten, twelve or fourteen of the new young shoots which were produced in the previous summer.

Blackcurrants

Once again, cut right down to the ground at planting to leave stubs of 7·5–10 centimetres at most. The following summer allow twelve–fourteen rods to grow which will bear fruit in the next season. Thereafter take out any old black wood at winter pruning, and retain some twelve–fourteen new young chestnut coloured rods. Try to keep the pruning low so that the new rods are produced at or below soil level. Feed and mulch well for good results.

Cherries

Cherries are easy to train on a wall or grow as free standing trees. They need little pruning other than an annual shaping in April to check extra long branches and remove awkward inward pointing or crossing branches. *Early Rivers* is a good variety, but needs another variety as a pollinator.

Damson

See plum – *Merryweather* is a good variety.

Gooseberries

One of the very best fruits for country winemaking, so if you have very limited space, plant gooseberries in the open garden before all other varieties of fruit. Gooseberries will crop in their first year. Take out crossing and downward facing branches thereafter during winter pruning, trying to keep space for a hand to gain access into the centre of the bush for picking to avoid being torn to pieces on the thorns, and trim back each side shoot to half way. Cut out old branches from time to time and grow on new young shoots. Feed well and mulch in summer.

Peach

Peregrine is the variety for outdoor walls as all other varieties need glasshouse protection. Try to establish a good fan-shaped system. Encourage a new shoot to grow beside each fruiting branch. Remove the old fruiting shoots each April and tie down the new ones in their places. Spray against *Peach Leaf Curl* in February with Dithane 495.

Plum

Everyone knows and loves the *Victoria* plum. I agree that it is a splendid fruit but personally prefer the *Purple Pershore* which ripens earlier and sets a great crop every year of glorious black/maroon plums with a rich sophisticated flavour and sweet skin. Tie several of the new long outward-facing shoots down in a wide arc with strings affixed to the stem of the tree to encourage fruit bud formation. Prune out any inward-facing and crossing branches in April. Buy *Victoria* on *Pixie* rootstock for dwarfed pot grown plum trees (Highfield Nurseries).

Raspberries

Cut down 7·5 to 10 centimetres at planting, the new canes will not bear in their first year. In the second year prune in January/

February to leave three or four good canes per plant and tie them in on to a three-wire trellis, cutting the tops level in February. Remove all fruit canes each year henceforth and tie in four to six new rods.

Training and pruning

The drawings illustrate better than words how to train your fruit trees, bushes and canes. The basic principle with bush and cane fruits is one of annual renewal of all wood or cane that has borne fruit, and the tying in of wood or cane that was newly produced in the previous summer. This pruning is done in the dormant season, preferably in January or, if you have a great deal to do, between mid-December and mid-February.

Raspberries are best pruned immediately after cropping; apple trees before March; and plums and cherries must only be pruned in April to try to avoid the introduction of the killer disease, *Silver Leaf Fungus*. In April the wounds swiftly heal and callous over.

Obviously trees are trained differently when planted against a wall from how they would be trained in an open free-standing situation, this is covered adequately by the diagrams.

Spraying

A simple spraying programme is outlined to take care of the more common fungal and insect pests. Space is at a premium here, so for advice in greater depth acquire a copy of the excellent Royal Horticultural Society book on fruit production.

Prevention rather than cure is vital, so a basic programme is covered. Obviously, if some problem takes hold, then the grower must take immediate curative action. You will need an upright sprayer, or a small knapsack model, with a lance to deliver the chemicals where they can be most beneficial.

Powdery Mildew is the most common problem, and this debilitating disease can be prevented by spraying with micronised sulphur, or Rubigan. Gooseberries and grapes are particularly at risk, also apples and stoned fruit.

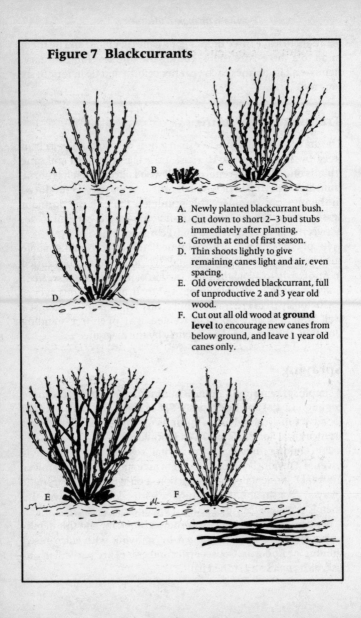

Figure 7 Blackcurrants

A. Newly planted blackcurrant bush.
B. Cut down to short 2–3 bud stubs immediately after planting.
C. Growth at end of first season.
D. Thin shoots lightly to give remaining canes light and air, even spacing.
E. Old overcrowded blackcurrant, full of unproductive 2 and 3 year old wood.
F. Cut out all old wood at **ground level** to encourage new canes from below ground, and leave 1 year old canes only.

Figure 8 Gooseberry

Gooseberry bush before and after winter pruning. Cut all the sideshoots back to 4–6 bud spurs, at the same time keeping the middle of the bush open and spurs facing upwards and outwards to facilitate harvesting and to allow sun and air into the bush centre to prevent mildew.

Figure 9 Blackberry, loganberry, tayberries etc.

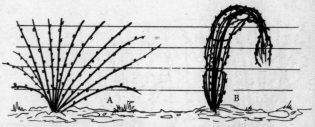

Train these canes on a series of horizontal wires. In autumn or winter remove all canes that have borne fruit and tie all the new canes as shown in B until spring, when they are released. Tie in a fan shape to the trellis to flower and fruit A.

Figure 10 Raspberries

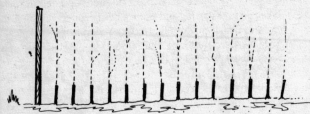

1   Cut back newly planted raspberry canes to leave 22 cm. Plant 44 cm apart.

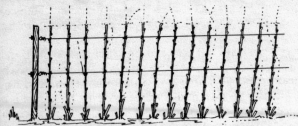

2   Following autumn tie one good strong cane on to wires and cut out all
    lesser cane growth at 8–15 cm above ground level. In following February
    cut out tops to 8–15 cm above top wire.

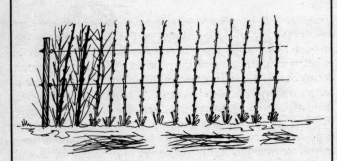

3   At end of second year, after cropping, cut out fruiting canes and all
    lesser canes; tie in one good *new* cane.

Dose: 55–85 grammes per 13 litres, applied every fourteen to twenty-one days. Plants are especially at risk in hot weather following a wet period. *Botrytis* is also a frequent and debilitating fungal disease, strawberries and grapes being especially at risk. Either Benlate, Bravo or Rovral are the preventative chemicals here; dosage 28 grammes per 13 litres, again applied at fourteen to twenty-one day intervals – can be combined with either the sulphur *or* Rubigan. Only use one of the chemicals specific against botrytis at a time and try to ring the changes rather than using one of the above choices right through the summer, otherwise a resistant strain of botrytis will emerge and you will lose control. Fruit may be eaten within twenty-four hours of being sprayed with Benlate, but the others should be left with a fourteen day gap from application to eating.

Honey Fungus is a real killer and can exist in old orchards and gardens as a mass of bootlace-like strands below ground which will search out and destroy new victims with remorseless certainty. It can also exist in old hedgerows. First indication is a clump of honey-coloured plate-like bracts of fungus which appear at ground level around the affected tree – this tree is sadly doomed. There is also a fungal development between the bark and the sap wood of the tree. Stricken trees must be cut down and burned, and then dig or burn out the roots to avoid spread.

Gooseberry Sawfly, Raspberry Beetle and insects on apples and stone fruit. Firstly try using Pyrethrum *or* Derris immediately the problem is noticed, dosage varies with different manufacturers so follow the instructions on the pack. Both these are plant based chemicals, harmless to the human body or digestive system, and harmless for your dogs and cats as well. Being simple chemicals, those mentioned are not systemic, and so must be applied more frequently than inorganic compounds – it is not safe to use systematic chemicals on fruit that is to be consumed or processed, for they stay in the sap system of the plant for several weeks.

Nicotine can be useful if your insect pests persist after an application of Pyrethrum or Derris. Collect up some cigarette stubs, or buy a couple of packets of twenty, and simmer them very gently for twenty to thirty minutes in half a litre of water. Add a quarter of the liquid to 4·5 litres of water and spray on to the insects. All should die for it is capable of killing the most persistant of pests – surely indicative of the harmful effects to the smoker!

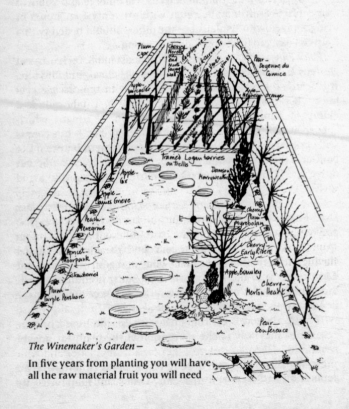

The Winemaker's Garden –

In five years from planting you will have all the raw material fruit you will need

4. Fruit Wines

 part from grapes, most fresh fruit forms the best base from which excellent wines may be made. Fruit must be clean and free from disease, and used as fresh as possible.

It should also be remembered that many fruits are not capable of making a balanced wine alone, so a combination of two or more different types of fruit is highly recommended. Experiment here with the fruit currently available, but do remember that when one of the components is an austere, bitter, acid, tannic fruit, like sloe or whortleberry (bilberry), do blend it with a soft, sweet and generous fruit to make a well balanced wine.

Richer, fuller flavoured wines are made by first crushing and then pressing the fruit, thereby obtaining a pure fruit juice ready to be fermented. For white wines one would first crush the fruit and then immediately press out the juice. This procedure can, of course, only be used on fruits without stones. In order to obtain sufficient depth of colour for red wines, one would firstly crush the fruit, and then ferment on the pulp for seven days to extract the richness of flavour from the base fruit, and also the colour from the skins and pulp. This system of winemaking necessitates having a fruit crusher and a small wine press – an outlay of some £150 to £200 at the time of writing. But this equipment will last for many years if well cared for – cleaned, kept in the dry and re-painted and varnished every year or two.

Though many people would consider this too high a price to pay for a moderate output of country wines each year, maybe several friends could club together for a fruit crusher and wine press, which would lower the cost considerably. Alternatively, a wine club could acquire a crusher and press, and then hire it out to members for a nominal fee. This equipment can, of course, be used for grape wine; and the press (and also the crusher if the correct type is bought) used to produce cider from the vast annual glut of apples that go to waste in countless orchards and gardens every year.

Caution – gravity, sugar and alcohol

When crushing and pressing fruit, you will obviously extract most of the natural sugar from the fruit – far more will be obtained than from steeping the fruit in water with its inherent dilution of the juice.

Therefore the gravity of the juice must be determined with a hydrometer, and correspondingly less Tate and Lyle added according to the reading obtained. For example, if your apples give a gravity of 40, you will add just 500 grammes of sugar per 5 litres since we aim for a starting gravity of 80 to give a final alcohol content of 10–10·5 per cent by volume. The sweeter the base fruit the higher the natural sugar content, and therefore less sugar needs to be added.

An alternative method to crushing and pressing is either cold or boiling water steeping in a vessel – these systems are used by most makers of country wines.

Cold steeping

When cold steeping fruit, one places the fruit in the container – an earthenware or polythene bowl or a polythene bucket (always be certain that it is food grade plastic); never use a metal container unless it is made from stainless steel. Cover the fruit with 3 litres of cold water for every 4·5 litres of wine to be made, and add either two crushed Campden tablets or 1 gramme of wine sulphur per 4·5 litres. Cover the vessel firstly with muslin and then a couple of layers of clean blanket material.

After twenty-four hours add the wine yeast, the juice of one to two lemons as suggested, a yeast nutrient tablet and then re-cover the vessel. Inspect and stir daily. Seven days later run the wine through a nylon or stainless steel sieve and into the fermentation vessel, into which you have previously poured 1 kilogramme of sugar per 4·5 litres. Fit a bung or cover with an air lock.

Follow directions hereafter as given in Chapter 2, remembering not to fill the fermentation vessel by more than three-quarters at this early stage to prevent overflowing.

Hot steeping

For steeping with boiling water, put the suggested quantity of fruit into the steeping vessel, and pour on 3 litres of boiling water for every 4·5 litres of wine being made. Cover with muslin and two layers of blanket, and allow it to cool to 65–70°C. This method automatically sterilises the fruit, so no sulphur or Campden tablet is required at this stage. Add the yeast to the pulp at 65–70°C, also the juice of lemons, if required, add some yeast nutrient, and then re-cover the vessel. Ferment on the pulp for a week, stirring daily, then strain off through your stainless steel or nylon sieve into fermentation vessels which have already been primed with 1 kilogramme of sugar per 4·5 litres of wine being made. Remember to fill them by no more than three-quarters to prevent wastage and mess due to overflows. Fit a bung and a fermentation lock, and then ferment out as outlined in the winemaking chapter.

In earlier times wines used to be made from various dried fruits and grains. These wines were perhaps popular because of their cheapness, and also the base materials were, and indeed still are, readily available in the depths of winter when fresh fruit was not available. These wines of course reflected the materials used in their making: raisins, sultanas, dates, dried apricots etc., definitely not such attractive flavours as those obtained from fresh fruits. Grains, such as wheat, tend to produce rather thick, dense, flat flavours. Today's trend is towards a fresh, delicate, youthful flavour in home winemaking, wines that lean, in style and character (though not necessarily flavour), more closely to commercial grape wines rather than trying to create bizarre, strange flavoured beverages of doubtful palatability.

Recommended fruits for winemaking

Fresh fruit	Amount per 5 litres	Sugar or grape concentrate	Lemon juice	Best blend with
Apples	3·5–4·5 kg	1 kg or 1 can Hock	1	Alone or with all others
Apricots	2–3 kg	1 kg or 1 can Sauternes	2	
Bilberries	1–2 kg	1 kg or 1 can Burgundy	1	Apples
Blackberries	2–3 kg	1 kg or 1 can Burgundy	2	Elderberries and Apples
Blackcurrants	1–2 kg	1 kg or 1 can Burgundy	1	Apples
Cherries	4·5 kg (sweet)	1 kg or 1 can Claret	2	
or	2 kg (Morello)	1 kg or 1 can Claret	2	
Damsons	1–2 kg	1 kg or 1 can Burgundy	1	Apples
Elderberries	2–3 kg	1 kg or 1 can Burgundy	1	Apples and Blackberries
Gooseberries	2–3 kg	1 kg or 1 can Hock	1	Elderflowers
Greengages	2–3 kg	1 kg or 1 can Sauternes	2	Apples and Elderflowers
Loganberries	2–3 kg	1 kg or 1 can Claret	2	Apples
Mulberries	4·5 kg	1 kg or 1 can Burgundy	2	
Oranges	20	1 kg or 1 can Hock		
Peaches	2–3 kg	1 kg or 1 can Sauternes	2	
Plums	2–3 kg	1 kg or 1 can Claret	2	
Raspberries	3 kg	1 kg or 1 can Claret	2	Apples
Redcurrants	3–3·5 kg	1 kg or 1 can Hock	2	Apples

Fresh fruit	Amount per 5 litres	Sugar or grape concentrate	Lemon juice	Best blend with
Rosehips	2 kg	1 kg or 1 can Sauternes	2	Apples
Sloes	2 kg	1 kg or 1 can Burgundy		Blackberries and Apples
Strawberries	2 kg	1 kg or 1 can Hock	2	Raspberries
Whitecurrants	3–3·5 kg	1 kg or 1 can Hock	2	Apples

Notes

Body. To add body to a wine, one should boil 1 kilogramme of bananas in 1 litre of water for half an hour. Add half a litre of the liquor so obtained to every 5 litres of wine – very useful if a full bodied, medium sweet wine is required.

Acidity. If a wine lacks acidity, one can either add the juice of another lemon or two, or dose with citric acid at the rate recommended on the package by the manufacturers.

Tannin. If a wine lacked astringency, tannin used to be added in the form of a cup of strong, cold tea; nowadays add a quarter teaspoon of powdered grape tannin to every 5 litres.

Fragrance or Bouquet. Preferably fresh or, alternatively, dried elderflowers are an excellent addition to most white wines, giving the wine a fresh, flowery, muscat-grape fragrance – a really professional touch. Especially recommended for gooseberry, apple, greengage, plum, and red and whitecurrant wines.

Grape Concentrate. Canned grape concentrate may be used to sweeten a fruit wine to advantage, since it provides more body, smoothness and flavour. Choose a type to suit the colour and style of wine.

5. *Flower Wines*

ines made from flowers should be absolutely exquisite, delicate and light with a fresh flowery nose. These wines can be made in the ancient traditional manner using just the flower water, sugar and yeast. Or they may be made to contribute towards more complex, richer wines of more weight and depth by using good white grape concentrate instead of cane sugar, and increasing the richness, and maybe the sweetness, by using raisins or possibly some fresh fruit. The options are endless, and the end results can be absolutely delicious.

Caution!

Extreme care must be taken to make sure the flowers used for making wine are free from any pollution or poisons. Flowers should *not* be gathered from roadside verges where they may have been splashed with petrol, oil, rubber and other pollutants in water spray from the road during and after rain. Carbon monoxide and lead from exhaust fumes are an added hazard. Care must also be exercised when collecting from farm hedgerows where pesticides and herbicides may have been used on the crops in that field to control insects and weeds. In general, where crops are grown, be they grain, vegetables or fruit, chemical sprays will have been applied, whereas in those fields that are used by grazing animals such as cows, sheep and horses, one can be fairly sure that the flowers will be free from harmful substances. Many sprays used on crops are harmless, but there are certain chemicals that are very persistent and could be present in a finished wine.

Always gather your flowers dry, preferably on a warm and sunny day, and also when they are fairly freshly opened and not tired and wilting. The flavour will be intensified up to the time of pollination; after this operation the flower has completed its purpose and will swiftly decline. Timing is therefore important.

Elderflowers

Elderflowers are valuable in that added to any wine they give an attractive muscat, grapey flavour – so once you find some suitable trees, those with small, delicate, lacy white flower heads (bushes which bear large plates of creamy flowers do not make such a delicious wine), you might perhaps collect as many as possible, strip the flowers off the green stalks, and dry them on clean paper or cloth laid out in the sun. Do not leave them out overnight. You may have to dry them gently in a cool oven if the weather is unkind at this time.

Elderflowers can henceforth be added to any wine you may wish to have enhanced by the spicy, muscaty flavour at the rate of 55 grammes per 4·5 litres. This process is particularly suited to the more delicate dry white wines where this flavour will best be appreciated. Why not collect one or two seedlings or suckers from the foot of a particularly suitable elder bush – as defined above – and plant it in a corner of your garden so you always have the flowers and fruit to hand, raised in a clean environment?

Flowers that can be used for making flower wines

Broom wine	4·5 litres broom flowers
Clover wine	4·5 litres clover flowers
Elderflower wine	2 litres elderflowers (the small white feathery type)
Primrose wine	3·5–4·5 litres primrose flowers

Method

Pick the flowers on a dry sunny day, gently pressing them into your measure to calculate volume. Use a half litre or litre jug. At home place them into a large vessel and cover with 3 litres of boiling water per 4·5 litres of wine to be made. Cover with muslin then a clean dry towel and finally a flat tray or similar to keep the cloth in place.

Stir daily for two or three days, then strain off into clean sterilised gallon jars or whatever vessels you use. Add the juice of 2 lemons and 1 kilogramme of cane sugar in cooled syrup form – alternatively a can of Hock or Moselle type grape concentrate instead of the sugar. Finally innoculate with a teaspoon of SIHA yeast, then fit a bung and air lock. Do not completely fill the vessels at this stage.

Keep the containers in a warm room until fermentation commences, then quickly remove the wine to a cooler atmosphere, preferably at about 50°F/10°C.

Watch your fermentation closely, and when it slows and ceases swiftly rack off the wine into new clean vessels. You must, at this stage, fill the jars right up with either new wine, older *delicate* white wine or with water. Refit the bung and fermentation lock, which should have been washed and refilled with 2 per cent sulphur solution. Keep the wine in the cool and rack every month, topping up the vessel each time. When the wine is still and clear either stand it outside in the cold for ten to fourteen days if the time of year is right, or cold stabilise in a refrigerator for fourteen days. This will usually complete the clearing process to a brilliant finish, dropping out any solids and hazes, and tartrate crystals if grape concentrate was used. These wines are best fermented right out to complete dryness.

These essentially delicate and fragrant wines do not need long maturing. As soon as they are clear they can be filtered and bottled. Choose suitable bottles for the type of wine – preferably green Moselle bottles, or failing this brown Hock bottles, or gold Chablis or Burgundy bottles.

Bottling

Wash the bottles with great care and examine for mould and cracks or flaws. Rinse with 2 per cent potassium metabisulphite and then put them upside down to drain. Assemble your Vinamat filter, remembering to pack and use the plates as advised in the section on filtering. Rinse with the 2 per cent sulphur solution and then flush through with 1–1·5 litres of water until the taste of paper has entirely vanished.

It is unlikely that it will be necessary to run these wines through coarse filter sheets since no fruit pulp, and its subsequent haze of minute particles in suspension, was used, so they can be run straight through the sterile sheets and bottled immediately.

Fill the bottles right up to the cork level, and once corked lay them away in the cool for at least six to eight weeks before drinking to allow them to recover from the rigours of filtration. Flower wines are suited to early bottling and being drunk young – within twelve to eighteen months of making. They are spring and summer wines, suited for drinking with light summer meals, and as an aperitif, lightly chilled, on a warm summer's evening.

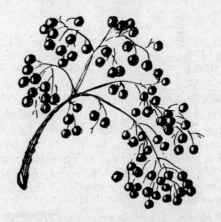

6. Silver Birch Sap Wine

his wine, reputedly a great favourite with Queen Victoria and made for her each year at Balmoral, can be very attractive. In very wet springs the sap is too plentiful and very thin and watery, and in a very dry spring the crop is too sparing to be viable. But in an average spring there is an opportunity for some individual, delicate and attractive wine to be made.

One has to tap the trees in the fortnight before leaf burst, as the sap is rising – once the leaves have burst forth the vigorous sap flow ceases. A difficult task, therefore, is ascertaining exactly when to tap your trees.

However, late March in an early spring, or early April in a later one, set forth armed with a sharp knife, one or more circles of flexible perspex some 50–60 millimetres in diameter and bent, after immersion in hot water, to form a lip, some grafting wax, hammer and nails and small plastic buckets or some kind of containers in which to collect the sap.

Cut a slanting vee-shaped groove out of the bark, being careful to cut no more than half way around the tree. Keep the cut no more than 10 millimetres wide and cut no deeper than through the bark. Make a deeper cut just below the lowest point of your vee and firmly push in the lip. If conditions are right the sap will begin to flow immediately. Hammer in a nail in a convenient place to allow the catching vessel to hang directly beneath the lip, but do not knock it in so deeply that it cannot be removed when your sap collecting is over. You may need to tap several trees according to how much sap you require. Collect your sap daily in a clean container.

Once the sap ceases to flow, remove the lip and the nail and fill the inscision with some grafting wax. Do not tap this tree again for at least two years.

When home, put the liquid in a saucepan and bring to the boil, but do not actually let it boil, then permit it to cool before transferring to a clean, sterilised fermentation vessel – fill to the three-quarters level at this stage.

Test the gravity and make up to 1,075 with cane sugar, add the juice of two lemons per 4·5 litres and some wine yeast.

Keep in a warm room until fermentation begins, then remove to a cooler area, ideally at 50°F/10°C.

Watch carefully as the fermentation slows and finally ceases, indicated to you by the slowing action in the fermentation lock. Immediately fermentation ends, rack the clearing wine from the sediment into a clean sterilised jar, fill to within 1 centimetre of the bung and refit the air lock to allow the CO_2 to continue escaping. A temporary revival of activity will occur due to the oxygen taken up during the racking operation. When the ferment stops, fill the jar right up with wine or water.

Rack and mature as with other wines, then stabilise, filter and bottle early. This wine is best drunk quite young, six to twelve months from making.

One could experiment, using silver birch sap as a base to which other ingredient flavours are added – elderflowers, primroses or possibly apples or apricots for example. But be careful not to swamp the delicate and special flavour of the sap by overdoing the other ingredients.

The sap is clear, so some colouring agent to induce a delicate hay colour could be a good idea – the flowers and fruits mentioned above would of course have this effect, or even grape concentrate. Again be very careful not to lose the delicate exquisite flavour of this wine that you have taken such trouble to produce.

7. *The Winemaker's Vineyard*

 rapes produce the ultimate in wine due to the fact that the grape possesses all the ingredients in the correct balance needed to make an excellent wine.

Grape juice is basically rainwater, taken up through the sap system of the vine by the roots, stem, branch, shoot and then finally stored in the grapes. The leaves, by a magical process known as photosynthesis, convert plant starches into sugar which is gathered and stored in the grapes. The ripening process occurs late, develops fast and enters a race against the weather – fine if the conditions during the last four, six or eight weeks from the beginning of August are hot, sunny and dry, but can be difficult – even hazardous – if the weather during this period is cold, wet and muggy.

All winemakers' gardens should have at least one vine – or perhaps a few vines trained to a South-facing wall or fence. Better still to plant two or three or more rows of vines provided with a trellis much like that erected for raspberries. Most varieties will, given a fair summer, produce some two-and-a-half to four bottles of wine each per annum on the trellis system; whereas on a wall a single vine can be allowed, or encouraged, to cover a vast area with the passing of time, and therefore can in due course produce a hundredweight or more of fruit every year. An exciting project? If so, please read on.

There are many, *many* varieties of grape vine, each differing in behaviour with regard to the type of grape and the subsequent wine produced; a wide range of ripening times from mid-September in the open vineyards to the end of October – even early November; crop per vine differs; and also the degree of resistance to mildew and botrytis, the two major foes of the English grape producer.

It follows, therefore, that there is more than likely to be one or more varieties of vine to suit most locations, and it behoves a potential vinegrower to discover which of these are most suited to his or her particular site, and by so doing pave the way for the greatest possible likelihood of success. A careful study of the range of vine varieties available – listed later in this chapter – is therefore most strongly advised.

After having read the following section on site preparation, the easiest method of explaining how to plant, train, prune, feed, spray and crop vines is to follow an imaginary year.

Site preparation

The protection offered by a garden holds warmth and aids fruit ripening, which enables grapes to be ripened in areas and at heights at which they might not normally succeed given an open field site.

In general a height of below 135–150 metres above sea level is recommended, and south of a line from Ipswich through to Worcester, the Vale of Evesham and down to a strip along the south coast of Wales is to be preferred. In very protected, warm sites considerably further north of this we hear of vines ripening their grapes satisfactorily: in North Wales, on the west coast of Wales, in Herefordshire, in Lincolnshire and South Yorkshire. The boundaries are ever being pushed further north and higher above sea level – but it must be stressed that this is when given a good site.

Vines like protection from the prevailing wind, but at the same time they need fresh air which much reduces the likelihood of the two major fungal diseases: mildew and botrytis. Noted frost pockets are not good sites, since the May frosts can burn off the entire crop of the current year in one night. Mild winter frost is beneficial since it propels the vine into a true and thorough dormancy – and indeed it is this dormant period in December, January and February which assists in the production of the fine, delicate, elegant wines of Northern Europe. Wines from areas with no true winter – like Algeria, Cyprus and to a lesser extent the South of France – reflect their origins by their high alcohol content, full, aggressive, often harsh flavours and a hot peppery finish.

However, extremely low winter frosts can cause damage to vines, at −15°C the sap stored in the roots for the winter can expand or even freeze and cause the roots to burst, and at −25°C bud and cane death can occur. Such very low temperatures, however, are rare in Britain, but we have experienced more extremely cold spells recently than on average: January/February 1963 springs to mind, also January 1981, January 1985 and February 1986 when temperatures as low as −27°C were recorded in several counties in a belt across southern England incuding Gloucestershire, north Somerset, Wiltshire, Oxfordshire, Berkshire, Worcestershire, Cambridgeshire and Essex − also of course further north of this line.

Ideally vines thrive best in a well-drained soil, sandy, gravelly, stony soils and silty clay loams − but if you are unfortunate enough to have a heavy clay, then this can be lightened by the digging in of organic matter: garden compost, strawy manure and sedge peat are all beneficial here. Vines produce a bigger crop of sweeter grapes from the poorer soils, they are best kept on the hungry side of well-fed after establishing themselves in their first year. Vines planted in a rich, deep soil tend to produce cane and leaf at the expense of fruit.

To sum up, vines will succeed best when planted below 120−150 metres above sea level; south of a line from Ipswich to Milford Haven; in a situation that offers protection from the prevailing winds yet allows good air circulation; avoiding obvious frost pockets; in free draining or improved soils; the rows, if planted in the open, running north to south to allow both sides of the vine to receive maximum heat and sun daily − this helps the grapes to ripen.

Trellis

There are many ways of supporting vines − please see the diagram on page 69 to appreciate the methods of training vines against walls or fences.

Vines in the open also require a support system. Again consult the training diagram to see which method appeals to you or lends itself to your particular garden. The cane pruning or *Guyot* system is the one most widely adopted in all France, Germany and Luxembourg and is recommended if you plan to plant two or three or more rows of vines. This system involves a removal of all the two-year fruiting wood, and tying down two young ripe canes each winter – a total renewal of cane. This keeps the vine young, vigorous and productive, and stimulates a good crop and the ripening of that crop. You can follow the progress of an average vine from planting to full maturity and cropping in the pages which follow.

Spacing

The width between your rows of vines is dictated by the method you plan to adopt to maintain weed control, be this a hoe, a garden rotavator, a mini or a full size tractor. Do not have your rows closer than a metre or so apart, so that adequate air circulation is permitted; wider than 2 metres and you lose the build up of heat within the vineyard, a feature known as 'micro-climate'. In certain circumstances vineyards are planted with rows 2·5, 3 or 3·5 metres apart, so that existing farm tractors can be used.

Leave 1 to 1·5 metres between the vines in each row – 1 metre for the European *Vinifera* varieties and 1·5 metres for the American hybrids, *Triomphe d'Alsace, Leon Millot* etc.

Planting

Vines may be planted from November through to the end of December. It is advisable to avoid January and also February if sub-zero temperatures are experienced. Planting can be resumed from March through until May once the frosts have disappeared.

The vineyard soil should be dug over well before planting, pulling out all perennial weeds. On a larger scale a rotavator will provide an excellent tilth. If you have a dry porous or sandy soil dig in some manure or compost to introduce organic material, and by so doing the water holding qualities are improved. Mark out the vine positions accurately with bamboos and nylon cord, checking that the squares and parallels are correct in both directions.

A handful of fish, blood and bonemeal mixed into the soil at the bottom of each planting hole to provide long-lasting slow release of organic nutrients is a recommended move, especially on the poorer soils.

Carry the vines during planting in a bucket of water to avoid the roots drying out. Prior to planting trim the roots to 7·5 to 10 centimetres long, and cut the top growth back to leave just two or three buds of new growth at the top.

Plant them deep enough so that only the top 5 or 7·5 centimetres are above ground level. This is important – many people put the roots just beneath the surface leaving all the vine above ground – should a dry windy spring be experienced the vines could easily die from lack of moisture; they just dry out and expire.

Keep an eye on your planting and line the vines up as you are putting them in. Firm in very well with your heel or boot so there is no possibility of rocking later on.

If a dry spring is experienced, water the vines every other day during any drought in their first year.

Training

Provide each vine with a bamboo at planting time. Soon after bud-burst visit all your vines and select the strongest, most upright and the best placed shoots to form the future leg of each vine; all lesser shoots are rubbed off to channel all the energy into the one master shoot. Tie in gently to the bamboo as it grows to prevent it being knocked off by the wind, dogs, cats, children etc. You can use plastic 'twistits' for this task – these are re-usable. You should aim to produce one good cane from each vine in the first year, the top of which *must* be pinched out at the end

Figure 12 Vine Training – Guyot, Goblet, Mosel Loop and Wall Vines

30 cm

30 cm

60cm ← 1.30 m →

A Newly planted vine with top just above ground.

B Train 1 shoot up a bamboo, tying in as it grows.

C Year 2 – January. Prune to leave 3 buds only.

D End year 2. Train 2 shoots in year 2. Tie into bamboos.

E Single Guyot. Prune in January year 3, cut 1 shoot to 3 bud spur, tie 2nd cane down on to lowest wire.

F End year 3. Note 3 replacement canes from spur, allow just 1 bunch per cane to develop and ripen.

G Year 4 – January. Prune, remove old fruiting arm.

H Cut central cane down to leave 3 bud spur; tie other 2 canes down either side of stem, each 60 cm long.

(1) GOBLET (2) MOSEL LOOP

J End year 4. Full double Guyot with 2 fruiting arms. Note 3 canes from spur. Allow 2 bunches per fruiting cane.

K Head or Goblet Training. No wires necessary. Allow 8–12 spurs at pruning.

L Tie shoots on to stake above vine as they grow, giving classic 'Goblet' shape.

M Mosel Loop. No wires. Keep just 2 long canes at winter pruning, tie them round and back on to vine or stake.

WALL TRAINED VINES

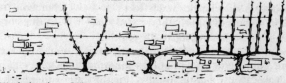

N Newly planted vine. Leave only top above soil level. Wires fixed to wall by 'vine eyes'. Feed well.

O Vine at end of year 1. Tie in for support as it grows.

P Tie the 2 canes down on to lowest wire, cut 1/3 off each.

R Allow 4 canes to grow upwards from these 2 arms. Stop off side shoots. Crop in 3rd year.

of August to encourage this cane to thicken, ripen and turn
brown before winter.

Spraying against mildew and botrytis

Look up Agricultural and Horticultural Sundriesmen and
Chemical Suppliers in your *Yellow Pages*, or visit your nearest
garden centre for small amounts if you have only a few vines.
Consult them for your supplies of micronised or liquid sulphur,
Zineb, Benlate, Bravo and Rovral. You will not need all these
fungicides at once, but establish a source of supply for the
future.

You must buy some micronised sulphur and 1 kilogramme of
Zineb for use in the first year of your vineyard. You will also need
a sprayer of some description with which to spray your vines. If
you have more than a few dozen vines the purchase of a
knapsack-sprayer is a worthwhile investment, whereas if you
foresee planting on a larger scale a mini-tractor is an excellent
device for which a multitude of attachments are now available,
including sprayers, rotavators, cultivators etc.

A fairly relaxed spraying programme is maintained during the
first two years of growth to keep mildew (*Oidium*) and botrytis
away, both of which, if allowed to gain hold of the vines, will
decimate and stunt growth and can kill young vines.

Oidium or powdery mildew is a grey dusting on the younger
leaves, and the grapes and grape stems on mature cropping
vines; the later really destructive stage is to firstly split the berries
which subsequently become dessicated to mere shells, which
then turn black and sooty. Botrytis is a grey mould, such as may
be found on strawberries and lettuces in wet weather, which will
attack the berries and the berry stalks and will, in due course,
cause the bunches to drop to the ground.

From the time the leaves are the size of a fifty pence piece, mix
up 55 grammes of sulphur and 28 grammes Zineb to a cream in a
small jug. This is poured into 7.5 litres of water and mixed well
before adding a further 7.5 litres to your container. This is
enough to fill a knapsack sprayer and the amounts can be scaled

down to suit the size of your equipment. The vines should be sprayed once every two weeks and do make sure the spray is applied to the *undersides* of the leaves which is where mildew and botrytis try to take a hold – spray applied to the upper leaf surface is unnecessary.

Incidentally, this spray is fine for keeping mildew off roses and blight from potatoes, so if you have any left over it need not be wasted.

Do not be put off by thinking spraying too arduous a task: once you have the sprayer and the chemicals it only takes a few seconds to spray each vine, and your plants will be healthy and free from fungal diseases. Do try and spray them every fourteen days – vines are particularly susceptible to disease during warm muggy weather and following heavy rainfall, and less prone during fine, fresh, dry, buoyant weather.

Spray programme for cropping vines

From the third or fourth year, your vines will begin to be allowed to bear fruit. The spray programme must be expanded to take great care that this precious crop does not become infected with either mildew or botrytis.

December Winter Wash – 2 per cent tar oil, also for apples, pears, plums etc. This will kill over-wintering insect eggs. It is actually of mixed use as it kills the good guys as well as the bad guys.

April/May (leaves 50p size) – spray with sulphur, Zineb and copper. The copper will kill off over-wintering spores of botrytis, phomopsis or dead arm, which are more likely to show up after a cool summer and a very rough winter, when the canes were perhaps less well ripened at the beginning of the cold weather.

Thereafter Every Two Weeks – spray with 55 grammes of sulphur, 28 grammes Zineb per 15 litres.

Last Week in June – spray with 55 grammes of sulphur and 28 grammes each of Zineb, magnesium sulphate, 28 grammes of copper sulphate, 28 grammes of boron (Solubor) and 28 grammes of either Benlate, Elvaron or Bravo in 15 litres of water. This is a pre-flowering spray designed to bring the vines into top physical condition prior to their most stressful time, ie. blossoming and berry set, by supplying them with certain minerals and trace elements vital to their well being and ability to set a full crop of grapes whilst also maintaining mildew and botrytis control. Remember, sulphur is specific against powdery mildew and Zineb against downy mildew.

Post-blossoming Spray – once flowering is over and the little white petals fall revealing minute green grapes, spray immediately with 55 grammes of sulphur, 28 grammes of Zineb + 28 grammes of *either* Benlate or Bravo (not Elvaron), whichever was not used prior to flowering, per 15 litres. One must ring the changes with the sprays against botrytis (i.e. Benlate or Bravo) so that the mould does not have a chance to build up a resistance against one particular chemical. This is very important. Make sure every bunch is soaked with spray, also the undersides of the leaves.

Following the application of the post blossoming spray, revert to the fortnightly application of the sulphur and Zineb until early September.

Pre-harvest Spray – 55 grammes of sulphur, 28 grammes of Zineb, 28 grammes of Rovral + 28 grammes of Fungex or Cuprokylt (copper) per 15 litres to toughen berry skins and bunch stems and by so doing discourage fungal attack.

This is a very important and critical spray application in that it has to keep the grapes clean for twenty-one vulnerable days up to the date of harvest. An added complication here is that all vines ripen their grapes on different dates, so one has to work out the likely date of picking for each variety and spray at exactly twenty-one days prior to that date. Please read the varietal ripening chart on page 73 for guidance here.

One can calculate the likely ripening date of each variety of vine by noting in your diary the date of *berry set*, which can range from the third week in June to the third, or even fourth, week in July, according to whether we have an early or a late spring.

Madeleine Sylvaner	55–60 days
Siegerrebe	60–65 days
Madeleine Angevine	70–75 days
Huxelrebe	70–75 days
Reichensteiner	75–80 days
Triomphe d'Alsace	80–85 days
Leon Millot	80–85 days
Muller Thurgau	90–100 days
Pinot Gris, Auxerrois	90–100 days
Pinot Noir, Chardonnay	90–100 days
Kerner, Ehrenfelser	90–100 days

The reason for this care is that the spray chemicals have a built in protection period against the fungi they control, and the armament against botrytis brought in at this last spray, namely Rovral, is effective for twenty-one days after which protection is lost.

The incidence of powdery mildew and botrytis is now far more likely with the shortening days, colder nights, greater possibility of rainfall and muggy weather of autumn. This is the reason for keeping back Rovral for this last spray, when the greatest protection is required.

November Spray – if you have the energy and the time, spray the vine canes after leaf fall with copper (Fungex, Cuprokylt or other) to toughen the canes so that they can better withstand the rigours of winter. This does much to prevent winter botrytis.

To sum up

Though all spray applications are incredibly important, it is absolutely vital to follow the guidance given for the April/May, Pre-flowering, Post-flowering and Pre-harvest sprays, all of which will give you great control over the health of your vines and should ensure that you pick ripe, clean grapes. Most chemicals can be purchased in 1 kilogramme packs which will last a small vineyard a long time. The majority of them are harmless, but should be kept safe and dry and out of the reach of children and pets. The user should wear Wellington boots, thick trousers or jeans, cover his/her arms and wear thick rubber gloves in case of any allergic reaction to any of these substances. If one is allergic, a simple gauze face mask is recommended, or even a rubber respirator can be purchased for some £7 or £8 from agricultural suppliers. The wearing of sun-glasses is an excellent idea if you find spraying an irritant to the eyes when using Elvaron, Bravo, Benlate and Rovral. Two final points; it is inadvisable to spray in high winds, and do not spray if rain is imminent since the chemicals are easily washed off, nor if it is very, very hot.

Second year January pruning

Vines are winter pruned in January if possible, for it is the only month when they are fully dormant. Do not, however, prune vines in sub-zero temperatures for they may well shatter and die back from the pruning cuts.

If your young vines have made light or moderate growth, prune them back to leave just a three bud stump near to ground level. This will encourage good root development, and inspire the vine to greater effort in the second growing season. If your yearling vines have made 1, 1·5, or 2 metres of growth, then you can cut back to the level of the bottom wire of your trellis. This will form the future leg of your vine.

Clear away all the prunings and burn them to eliminate all the botrytis spores that exist on thin, unripe wood.

Second year training

In the second year allow two canes to grow on all vines other than those that were really weak and poor at the close of the first year's development. One of these canes will bear your first light crop in the third year.

Tie the canes in to their bamboos as they grow to prevent wind damage. Maintain a regular spraying programme.

When the canes reach 15 centimetres above the height of your trellis, nip out the tips of the growing shoots, this encourages the canes to thicken and ripen and become woody before winter.

Third year

Most vines will have produced two good canes of some 120 to 180 centimetres in height in the second year, canes that were topped in late August or September and had a chance to thicken and harden during the autumn. Any vines that made poor growth should again be cut back to a stub with three or four buds.

Winter pruning – January

Look at each vine very critically. Select the cane best placed to be the future leg or stem of the vine: the cane that is straight, stout and in line with the row. Cut this cane to height of the bottom wire of your trellis and then clip or tie it on to the supporting bamboo. The second cane is taken up to the bottom wire, gently bent every few inches into a gradual semicircle up, over and back down to the bottom wire again, and is then clipped or tied to this wire. The length of this first fruiting cane is determined by the length of the ripe, hard, green cored wood. Some can be cut to a full 60 centimetres in length, others a mere 13 to 30 centimetres. Ripe wood is brown, beige or fawn; unripe wood is white or dull grey, often with black blotches which are overwintering botrytis spores known as sclerotica. The colour of unripe wood when cut is not green but brown or beige in section.

Caution

Do not be tempted to ask vines to crop that are too poorly developed to do so. Vines need to make a considerable root system before bearing fruit, and once established the stem becomes woody, firm and swells annually. The fruiting cane should be of a pencil thickness. If any vines are not up to scratch, cut them back to a single short stem of some two, three or four buds, and then they may well catch up by the fourth year. Bear in mind that most French growers would never consider allowing any of their vines to crop until the fourth year – this is the rule in Bordeaux, Burgundy and Champagne.

Budburst – disbudding

Budburst will occur from late April to mid May, depending upon year and location. When the shoots are some 5–7·5 centimetres long, go over each vine and rub off all shoots at ground level and up the stem. Check the shoots on the tied down fruiting cane, rub off the smaller of any twin buds and, after having checked that the shoots you leave have one or two embryo flower bracts (it is no use leaving barren shoots to develop), rub off all but a maximum of six or seven upright facing shoots. The number of shoots left should be decided by the length of the fruiting cane – a cane of only 15 centimetres can only stand two or three shoots; leave the top two or three shoots on the leg to develop, rub off all others.

Apply a sulphur/Zineb/copper spray once the leaves reach the size of a fifty pence coin; copper to kill any overwintering botrytis and phomopsis (dead arm) spores.

Training

As these fruiting shoots develop, tuck them between the first and then the second pair of double wires of your trellis. Once they are 15–20 centimetres above the top double wires, pinch out the growing tips. This stopping will hopefully be achieved just before blossoming, which greatly assists a high level of pollination.

Pre-blossoming spray

Apply the pre-flowering spray cocktail (refer to above section on sprays) within the seven–ten days prior to the commencement of flowering. In an early year flowering can begin as early as 15–21 June, but this is very rare indeed – we experienced this in 1976 and in 1984. Blossoming usually starts from 7 July in an average year, and from 14 July in a very late spring/summer. Do not forget to note the dates upon which your different varieties achieved berry set.

Do *not* spray during flowering.

Post-blossoming spray

Apply the post-flowering spray immediately the blossoming is finished, indicated by the minute pollen-bearing stamens dropping off and the berries beginning to swell.

Side shooting

Once the vines have their tops stopped or pinched out, side shoots begin to develop apace. These should be nipped off between finger and thumb *after the first leaf* (or use secateurs). These two pruning actions concentrate the energy of the vine into successful pollination and fruit development rather than unchecked miles of cane and acres of leaf.

Vines should be maintained as neat hedges from this stage on, little more than 30 centimetres wide in section and some 1·5 metres in height. A useful yardstick here is to remember that the vine requires no more than twelve – fourteen leaves per fruiting cane to develop and ripen grapes.

Photosynthesis

The leaves can be likened to sugar factories; they absorb sunlight and heat which is accumulated in the leaves as starch and transferred to the grapes where it is stored as sugar. The leaves immediately above, around and below the bunches of grapes are the most valuable here. The growing tip and side shoots *take* energy rather than give it, hence the recommendation for their

removal. You may have to side shoot and top the vines three or
four times in all.

Pre-harvest spray

Check the dates upon which your vine varieties set their berries
and work out the likely picking dates using the table given above.
Apply the pre-harvest spray twenty-one days before the esti-
mated harvest date for each variety. This is a very vital spray
since the vine and its precious fruit are more likely to fall prey to
botrytis now than at any other time. This is due to the shorter
days, greater humidity, damp, rain and cooling temperatures of
early autumn. It is a tragedy when a potentially excellent crop is
lost in the fortnight before picking due to lack of care at this time
– twelve months' work lost. So many vinegrowers fall into this
trap, even so-called professionals with commercial vineyards. Do
not be tempted to drop this final spray even if the weather is
marvellous, hot and dry. Ripening, sweet, thin-skinned grapes
are the most vulnerable of all fruit to fungal rot, and rot they will
if not fully protected.

Fourth year vines

The grower will have encouraged three good canes to grow from
the top three shoots on the new vine leg or stem, these three will
form firstly the new spur (from which three canes will grow in
the following year) and, secondly, in the fourth year *two* fruiting
canes can be tied down on to the bottom wire on either side of
the stem. A look at the sketches of a vine's development from the
time of planting to the fourth year will illustrate the training and
pruning during these early, formative years far better than any
written description.

Winter pruning

This should be undertaken in January/February – but never in
sub-zero temperatures.

Disbudding

A mature vine, from the fourth year onwards, can carry a maximum of twelve–fourteen fruiting shoots, plus the three shoots left to develop from the spur. Two bunches of grapes per fruiting shoot are sufficient for the vine; remove the third and smallest before blossoming.

Weak vines

If you have a weak vine or two that fail to make sufficient cane and height to crop in the third and fourth years, be patient. Cut them down to two, three or four buds, or back to the stem (*cep* in France), leaving a three-bud spur. These slow vines generally make it in the end, but if they look too poor to ever catch up, dig them up and replace with young, vigorous vines.

Weed control

Weeds must be eliminated otherwise they compete with the vines for nutrients, and also maintain a damp, humid blanket over the soil in which mildew and botrytis spores will lurk ready to infect your vines when the ideal conditions present themselves.

The vineyard floor should be kept free of all weed growth. Ideally a frequent hoeing to keep weeds away is the very best form of control for the garden vineyard. A rotavator run up and down the rows to just knock over the weeds is the answer for the larger vineyard.

Weedkillers (herbicides) should not be used amongst vines less than three years old. If you have some persistent perennial weeds such as docks, thistles or nettles, buy a litre of Roundup and dilute this at a rate of 55 grammes to 4·5 litres of water, and just touch spray the actual weeds. This should kill them with one application, but a second may be necessary. Roundup is also useful for paths, drives etc. but will kill any green plant it touches, so take great care, especially with young vines.

Nutrition

Vines crop better and produce finer, sweeter grapes when kept on the hungry side of well fed. An annual application of two handfuls of sulphate of potash per vine is advised, spread over a radius of some three to four feet around each plant. This chemical encourages the formation and ripening of fruit and the ripening of the vine canes or wood before winter. A handful of super-phosphate per vine assists photosynthesis, the conversion of sunlight via the leaves into starch and then subsequent formation of sugar which is stored in the ripening grapes.

Harvesting

If possible, always harvest in dry weather. Grapes, being spherical, have a large surface area and it is surprising how much water will cling to the skins, diluting the wine quite considerably. Use a pair of secateurs or special grape picking scissors to sever the bunches – pulling will only cause grapes to drop from the bunch on to the ground since the stalks of nearly all varieties are surprisingly tough. Collect in clean baskets or buckets and process the grapes as soon as possible.

Recommended white wine grape varieties

French

Auxerrois. This variety is popular in Luxembourg and in Alsace and is probably a sort of clone of Chardonnay, but ripens earlier. It bears a light to moderate crop of clean, firm, fairly open bunches and has good botrytis resistance both on leaves and bunches. It makes a crisp, clean, flinty, elegant wine when used alone, similar to Chablis or white Burgundy. Blends well with Chardonnay, Pinot Gris, Pinot Meunier and Pinot Noir.

Chardonnay. The classic noble variety grown in France for Champagne, Chablis and White Burgundy, this vine ripens too late in

England other than in the hottest, most favourable sites, but would ripen on a hot South-facing wall, or in a glasshouse or polytunnel in most areas. Moderate to heavy cropper, with good leaf and bunch resistance to botrytis. Makes a very superior wine indeed, providing acidity is reduced prior to fermentation with Acidex if necessary.

Gewurtztraminer. Also grown in Germany, this variety is very popular in Alsace in Eastern France. Growth is strong; good disease resistance due to glossy round leaves and tough grape skins. The grapes ripen too late in the open other than in highly favoured sites or on walls, in glasshouses or polytunnels. Wine is highly individual, attractive, spicey, rich, honeyed, with a lemon finish on the palate.

Madeleine Angevine. The most superior vine available in Britain with regard to growth, excellent flower set, good yield (up to 3·8 bottles/vine) ripening late September/early October, high natural sugars and ability to make a beautiful dry, crisp, fruity wine similar to a Chablis, still Champagne or an Alsatian wine. Excellent wood ripening, a vital feature for consistent, reliable performance; good disease resistance, easy to look after. Highly recommended.

Madeleine Sylvaner. An old French variety, the earliest to ripen its grapes in Britain. Growth moderate, loves a clay soil, prone to botrytis infection due to grapes being very thin skinned, so a tight spray programme is advised. Wine delicate, crisp, light and flowery – could be described as heavenly. Suitable for the higher, cooler, more exposed Northerly situations. Good wood ripening.

Pinot Gris (Rulander). A vine of moderate growth and yield, produces bunches of grey/pink grapes that ripen by mid October. Excellent disease resistance similar to all the Pinots. Best blended with Chardonnay, Pinot Meunier and Pinot Noir, which together create a classic elegant, fresh dry Alsatian type wine. Excellent wood ripening.

Pinot Meunier (black). This vine is grown in the Champagne area as the third grape used for Champagne production. Again a hard wooded vine and although the leaves have a downy underside they do not seem to attract botrytis. The grapes from this variety are more suited to the production of white wine than red wine in Northern Europe as the skins do not have much colour pigmentation. Grapes ripen mid/late October. A beautiful wall vine with highly attractive leaves.

Pinot Noir. Again a black grape, but together with Chardonnay, this is the second main grape used in the production of Champagne. A moderate to heavy cropper, all pinots set well during blossoming, grapes ripen by mid/late October, excellent wood maturing. Best suited to white wine production. Highly recommended.

Seyval Blanc. A French hybrid vine (a cross between a European *Vitis vinifera* and a native American vine: bred in France between 1860/1880) which thrives best on an alkaline soil – vigour very variable from site to site, yields also vary, can develop *coulure* (a browning and shrivelling of the floret) during flowering if the weather is cold and wet at this time. Useful to grow to produce grapes with a high acid content to add to the two Madeleines, Reichensteiner or Siegerrebe must after a hot, hot summer to enable the grower to allow later varieties to become super-ripe on the vine – their acidity drops too low in such a summer and should be raised to 9–10 expressed as tartaric by a transfusion of a high acid juice. Excellent wood ripening.

German

Bacchus. Moderate vigour; attractive leaves; good set; moderate yield of grapes that ripen in mid October to make a spicy, mellow, very German wine. Good wood ripening.

Ehrenfelser. A Riesling cross, a very neat, uniform vine producing, tight, clean cylindrical bunches of grapes that ripen by mid/late October, usually with a high acidity. Wine is almost pure Riesling in flavour, and is best made by blending with grapes from Kerner and Scheurebe and, from exceptional sites only, grapes from Riesling vines. This vine needs an excellent, early site and shows good wood ripening.

Huxelrebe. A poor, stony, rocky, gravelly or sandy soil is a necessary factor required to check the excessive, soft growth that this vine will diplay on rich, deep soils. Huxelrebe will overcrop, if permitted, at the expense of the crop the following year, so one must reduce their fruiting shoots in the spring, and reduce the bunches to two per shoot. Produces massive bunches which are botrytis prone when ripening, so good spray cover is vital. Wine rather pungent when young, improves with age.

Kerner. This is the best Riesling cross, showing moderate vigour, it always sets well during flowering, produces a regular crop of clean, firm grapes, and the wood from this vine is always iron hard and nut brown by September/October. Great resistance to botrytis with hard, dark green leaves. Mid/late October ripening means this variety is suitable only for hot, southerly sites. Highly recommended.

Optima. Another Riesling cross, produces grapes that make a lovely Riesling-style wine, but without the good wood ripening and botrytis resistance demonstrated by Kerner above. Ripens by mid-October and needs vigilant spray control to bring grapes to the point of harvest in a botrytis-free condition. Optima produces a most attractive wine; blends well with Kerner and Scheurebe.

Reichensteiner. Initially a weak grower, but comes into full production in the fourth year. Has a rather shrubby growth habit in colder years, Reichensteiner flowers and sets magnificently and ripens its beautiful clean, open bunches by early to mid-October very adequately. Good resistance to bunch botrytis, its only drawback is poor wood ripening and therefore winter wood is botrytis prone; after a poor summer it is *sometimes* difficult to find two good canes to tie down for the following year. Wine is delicate and rather recessive; blends very well with Madeleine Angevine and other wines. Recommended.

Riesling. Only worth attempting in the open on exceptional sites, but given the protection of a South-facing wall, a glasshouse or a polytunnel, this vine is a real winner. A vine of moderate vigour; moderate to good production; excellent blossoming and setting potential; excellent botrytis resistance and wood ripening; a real growers vine. Late October ripening on exceptional sites after a heatwave summer, otherwise too late in the open. Wine quality is second to none.

Scheurebe. All descriptions of the Riesling apply to Scheurebe. It is a Riesling cross that flowers and sets very well, produces big bunches and displays excellent wood ripening. Only drawback is late ripening, but with acid reduction of the must a very beautiful Riesling style wine can be produced. Blends well with Kerner, and Ehrenfelser. Needs a superb site, or, preferably, a South-facing wall, or a glasshouse or polytunnel.

Siegerrebe. This is the perfect vine in all but one respect, a tendency towards poor setting during flowering if the weather conditions are less than ideal at this time. Shows a moderate growth habit and the potential for producing four bottles of wine per vine in a good year when fruit set is high – without overcropping. The second earliest vine to ripen its grapes, which can be by mid-September, usually by 21–28 September in Southern England. Grapes will ripen 100 per cent, so no added sugar is necessary, but the acidity usually drops too low so that the addition of some 10–15 per cent of a high acid juice (Seyval, Riesling or Scheurebe) is necessary to create a sound, well-balanced wine with keeping properties. Grapes ripen to a beautiful pinky/old-gold colour and make excellent eating – a dual purpose grape.

Recommended red wine grape varieties

None of the classic French red wine grapes will ripen in the open in Britain, the only way to grow them is to plant them under glass or in a polytunnel. We have to look for earlier ripening varieties that will give the necessary depth of colour, a real red wine flavour, and the required fruit, acid and tannin input to give the wine the required keeping properties. There are two vines from Alsace that display these qualities.

Leon Millot. A vine of good vigour, 100 per cent resistance to botrytis due to the glossy, dark green leaves, superb early wood ripening and the thick skins of the grapes. Flower set is always 100 per cent, and the big, cylindrical bunches ripen by mid October. Best wine is made with a blend of 30–40 per cent Leon Millot/60–70 per cent Triomphe d'Alsace. Ferment wine for seven days on the skins, no more and no less, and keep for one to two years in bulk before bottling so that you can produce a full-bodied, mellow wine of great substance with a glorious deep red colour that will keep for years.

Triomphe d'Alsace. Similar to Leon Millot, this vine demonstrates good vigour and, due to the shiny, dark green leaves, superb wood ripening and thick skinned grapes, is also 100 per cent resistant to botrytis. However, flower set can be severely affected if it is cold during blossoming and from 25–75 per cent *millerandage* or 'hen and chickens' effect in the bunches (a few normal but mostly pinhead berries) can be experienced; a minimum night and day temperature of 10°C (50°F) seems to be the critical level. All comments on winemaking apply as described under Leon Millot. My vines, now in their eleventh year, have been producing an increasingly superior wine from this blend; initially rough, raw and fiery, but with vine age, by the eighth year, a superb wine has been the reward for patience.

The Austrian *Blauberger* may have excellent qualities for red wine production in this country, but is, as yet, unproven. Another Austrian variety, *Zweigeltrebe*, has proved disappointing other than for white or rosé wine production. The wine is too earthy, thin and austere for red wine. We are also looking at other red wine grape varieties which are on trial here, mostly new German hybrids. *Dornfelder* appears to be a winner.

Vines and grapes are the most rewarding and exotic of all fruit producing plants. For an in-depth treatise on their culture read *Vinegrowing in Britain* by myself, published by J. M. Dent & Son Ltd.

8. *Grape Winemaking*

rapes must first be crushed before pressing can take place. To achieve this end a grape crusher or berry mill is necessary – failing this tread the grapes in a half cask or large polythene tub until every berry is burst. It is important to appreciate that the grapes merely need to be burst and not ground to a pulp.

White grape wine

Transfer the grape pulp to a cleaned and sterilised wine press, the basket of which has been lined with strong nylon curtain netting material – this is to prevent the grape pulp from blocking the gaps between the press basket slats, and also to contain the pips and skins so that they are not forced out between the staves. Be certain to pack the basket evenly with pulp, omitting this precaution can cause a crooked pressing and dangerous pressures can build up in the press. Apply pressure gently for a steady flow and transfer the juice to a clean and sterilised vat or jar. It is better and easier to turn the press down hard and then to leave it for five minutes, this permits the juice to run out and relieves the pressure, thereby making it once again easy to turn the screw. Fill the containers and seal.

When the last drop of juice has been extracted, the time has come to open and empty the press. Remove the semi-dry cake and break it up really well into small pieces. This should now be pressed a second time – a good plan is to carry out two first pressings, and then combine the pulp from these for a second pressing. Two pressings produce a viable yield, but it is neither advisable nor economic to press further.

Test the gravity of your juice with the hydrometer. For white wines the nearer the specific gravity is to 80 the better, from 75 to

80 no Tate and Lyle need be added. If you have the necessary kit you should be able to test the acidity of the juice, which should ideally be between 9 and 11 tartaric.

Leave the juice twelve to twenty-four hours to clear, all the minute solid particles will drop to the bottom of the tank and form a sediment.

Carefully syphon or pump the now clear juice off the sediment into a clean, sterilised container, remembering not to fill it more than 7/8 full at this stage to leave room for a vigorous fermentation.

Add Acidex to reduce the acidity if necessary – there will be instructions on the packet, but if in doubt read the section on stuck fermentation in the chapter on Winemaking (Chapter 2). Next pour in the Tate and Lyle if any is needed – please consult the table at the end of this chapter which will help you to determine exactly how much sugar to add to your juice for a given alcohol content in the end product.

Lastly add the wine yeast – I cannot recommend the German SIHA yeast highly enough, it has revolutionised my own wine making. Swiss Novo yeast is also excellent.

Fit an air lock, and if the temperature is not too cold, fermentation should commence in one to three days.

Variations on white grape wine production

Late Pressing. From Germany we learn that they are experimenting with leaving the crushed grape pulp for twelve hours before pressing, the skin contact leads to more flavour and colour in white wines. To keep the pulp fresh and free from oxidation (browning) or acetification (attack by vinegar bacteria) sprinkle 5 grammes of wine sulphur over each tub of pulp.

Fermenting on the Pulp. Secondly, the Germans are also experimenting with white wine fermented on the pulp, as with red wine – before backing this suggestion I would recommend that winemakers try a batch system here:

a Batch 1–whole fermented on pulp for seven days
b Batch 2–75 per cent fermented on pulp for seven days and blended back into the 25 per cent that was pressed straight away
c Batch 3–50 per cent fermented on pulp, 50 per cent pressed immediately and then blended after seven days
d Batch 4–25 per cent on pulp, 75 per cent immediate pressing and then blended after seven days
e Control – wine made by pressing immediately after crushing

Caution. I would recommend that you process 80–90 per cent of your yield by the control method and keep the trials to very small batches of a few gallons until you are sure of what you are doing. Assess the comparative quality of each batch from fermentation through to the finished, bottled wine and be very sure you like the product of pulp fermentation before committing a large or total percentage to the new method.

Racking. Make a real effort to catch the wine at the cessation of the first fermentation and rack it immediately. The activity in the air lock will slow and then cease – a sure indication that the wine has fermented out most or all of the sugar.

Pump or syphon the wine into a clean, sterilised container, which can now be topped up almost to the level of the fermentation lock. The action of racking will induce a slow, gentle fermentation as the last of the sugar is used up. Rack thereafter once per month until bottling, now topping the containers up to the bung.

Dry, Medium or Sweet Wine? If a dry wine is wanted, allow the ferment to continue naturally until the specific gravity has dropped out to 0·995. Such a wine presents no problems, is totally stable in so far as there is no sugar left for any yeast to feed upon, and after cold stabilisation it will be ready for bottling.

A Medium Wine. Once the gravity has dropped to between 2·0 and 7·0, the wine must be racked immediately and heavily dosed with 50 ppm (parts per million) of wine sulphur to prevent further fermentation. The wine is next cold stabilised by exposure to frost, or placed in a cold cabinet for fourteen days to clear. The alternative is to allow the wine to ferment out to total dryness and then to introduce at the time of bottling 5 per cent of filtered, sulphured, sweet unfermented grape juice (sweet reserve) that you kept back at harvest for this purpose.

Sweet Reserve. Select some very ripe grapes of the same variety as those you wish to make into a medium or sweet wine. Crush and press these grapes and stand the sulphured juice for twenty-four hours to settle and clear, then rack the juice off the sediment. Sulphur to 20 ppm and then filter the sweet juice into clean 1 gallon plastic containers, filling no more than seven-eighths full. Place them in a deep freeze until needed.

An alternative is to grow a row or two of Ortega vines (as they do in Germany) and use these early ripening grapes for your sweet reserve – other possible varieties are Madeleine Sylvaner and Siegerrebe.

Bottling with Sweet Reserve – Medium White Wine. First run the dry white wine to be bottled through coarse filter sheets. Check the free sulphur dioxide level and adjust to 50 ppm. Immediately before you bottle, add your sweet reserve at a ratio of 5 per cent to the bulk of the wine and make sure it is thoroughly mixed. Filter straight away through sterile filter sheets into clean, sterile bottles, cork and bin in the cool and dark. I cannot over-stress the importance of making certain everything is clean and completely sterile, for any micro organisms will be sure to start a fermentation in the bottle as soon as the weather warms up in the summer with subsequent formation of sediment in the bottle and possible (if not probable!) explosions.

Bottling with Sweet Reserve – Sweet White Wine. As above, coarse filter the wine to be bottled, check the free SO_2 and adjust to 50 ppm. Immediately prior to bottling add sweet reserve at a ratio of 10 per cent to the bulk, and do make sure that it is very well mixed before you continue. Also add 200 milligrammes per litre of potassium sorbate as an added protection against any fermenting in the bottle. Sterile filter immediately into clean sterile bottles, cork and store away in the cool and dark.

Note. After bottling wine becomes unfit to drink for at least six weeks, so allow time to elapse before you start drinking the wine – eight weeks is really the minimum. Filtering is a tortuous process for a wine, the bouquet and more subtle flavours are severely depressed and need time to re-assert themselves. You will notice that the wine improves and alters quite noticeably as it ages in the bottle.

Red grape wine

Run the grapes through the grape crusher, or tread them thoroughly. Put them in one or more large vessels with wide openings at the top, and preferably with a tap at the bottom.

Tip in the first crushing and then add the wine yeast before filling up to no more than three-quarters full with more grape pulp. Cover the top with a clean sterile cloth and then rest the lid on top but do not screw it down.

Before fermentation begins you must test the specific gravity of your juice. Red wines need an initial gravity of 95+, so if the gravity is less than this figure make a careful note of it so that later, when the juice has been extracted and the volume assessed, you can work out exactly how much Tate and Lyle to add by reference to the chart at the end of this chapter.

A 'cap' of grape skins will quickly form as the fermentation speeds up: the carbon dioxide given off by the yeast brings this to the surface. This must be pressed down and turned at least twice daily during the full seven day period of pulp fermentation. This not only aids colour and flavour extraction but also prevents the pulp from acetifying. Watch out for the fumes as you bend over the vat to carry out this procedure!

At the end of seven days, if you have a tap at the bottom of your vat, run off the juice into a clean, sterile container. Then bucket, or somehow dip out, the pulp (or pulp/juice mixture if you have not already separated them) into your clean and sterilised wine press, the basket of which has been lined with a clean sheet of nylon netting. Apply steady pressure to the press, and be ready to swap and empty buckets quickly as the juice initially runs out at a tremendous pace. Do not press red wine pulp a second time otherwise a rather nasty, pithy bitter flavour can be extracted. Remember not to fill the fermentation vessels more than three-quarters to seven-eighths full.

Assess the quantity of juice obtained and, if necessary, add the Tate and Lyle now. The table at the end of the chapter informs you of how many kilogrammes/grammes to add to a given volume of juice in litres to achieve an agreed alcohol content in the finished wine.

Ferment the wine out to dryness, then rack, afterwards topping up the vessel(s) to the level of the bung. Rack thereafter every two months, again topping up the container each time.

A red wine of a poor year made from unripe grapes is never going to be a great wine, so a wine such as this can be bottled at six months old. However, a wine produced in a heatwave summer, made from grapes that achieved 80+ gravity, even 94–97 as our grapes did in 1984, should have sufficient colour, depth of flavour and character to make a really good wine which will merit keeping in bulk for twelve to eighteen months providing you keep the container topped up regularly and racked every two and then every three months.

Bottling. Red wine is a far more stable, robust product than white wine, and requires less preparation for bottling. A lower SO_2 level is required for red wines, 20–25 ppm is adequate, and only a coarse filtration to polish up the brightness and remove the solids. Do please use green (or anyway dark) bottles for your red wine – clear or light bottles will allow the colour to fade. As mentioned above, you should leave the bottles in the cool and dark for two months after bottling before thinking about drinking – in fact wine from a good year will continue improving for many years so do not drink it all at once.

For White Wines. To raise juice to 80° specific gravity, 10·9 per cent alcohol by volume, add to each batch of 100 litres of juice the amount of Tate and Lyle shown on this table:

Initial specific gravity	Kg sugar (1 kg = 2·2 lb)
50	7·5
52	7·0
54	6·5
56	6·0
58	5·5
60	4·9
62	4·4
64	3·9
66	3·4
68	2·9
70	2·4
72	1·9
74	1·5
76	1·0
78	0·5

NB Some varieties will achieve an SG of 80° on the vine, e.g. Siegerrebe, and will therefore require no added Tate and Lyle.

For Red Wines. To raise juice to 93° SG, 12·0 per cent alcohol by volume, add to each batch of 100 litres of juice the amount of Tate and Lyle shown on the following table:

Initial specific gravity	Kg sugar (1 kg = 2·2 lb)
50	11·0
52	10·5
54	9·9
56	9·4
58	8·8
60	8·3
62	7·8
64	7·3
66	6·8
68	6·3
70	5·7
72	5·2
74	4·7
76	4·2
78	3·7
80	3·2
82	2·7
84	2·2
86	1·7
88	1·2
90	0·7
92	0·2

9. *Cider and Perry*

ider, 'the White wine of England', and one of the oldest of our national beverages, can so very easily be made by anyone providing they have access to windfall apples and a cider or wine press.

Cider used to be made on thousands of farms in England and Wales, particularly in the West Country – Devon, Somerset and also Gloucestershire and Herefordshire, and to a lesser extent in the counties bordering those named. Kent and East Anglia also have a long tradition of cider production. This tradition existed as a part of the farming year until the 1939–45 war, though a handful of farms continued cider making into more recent times.

We learn that cider is the name given to the product from the first and second pressings when pure apple juice is obtained from the press. After these two pressings the farmer then used to steep the pulp removed from the press in water in open half-casks over-night. The following day this revitalised pulp was pressed again and a far thinner, more watery juice with a lower sugar content was produced. This fermented out with half the sugar content of the first pressings and was named 'small cider' which was always drunk by the following harvest in August or September since the alcohol content would not permit it to keep for any longer.

The small cider used to be made available to the men in the fields during hay-making and harvest time, and also formed part of their wages, so it was in the interest of all of them to make as much as possible and to make it well. The cider was, of course, also enjoyed by the farmer, but if the operation was run on a commercial scale it was the cider that was sold as a product with an alcohol content ranging from 5 per cent after a moderate summer, to 7–10 per cent after a really hot summer.

All these farms had large old orchards with a wide range of apple tree varieties, usually near to and around the farmhouse where they offered shelter from the elements to the buildings and were used as a warm nursery for the ewes and lambs during the spring, and later maybe for a mare and foal or the spring turn-out of young calves.

Some orchards were solely planted with apple trees; there were usually a few eating apples, a few to provide cookers for the kitchen and the rest being a range of cider varieties: sharps, bitter-sharps, bitter-sweets and sweets. The juice from these specially selected types of apple making a rich, well balanced cider with sufficient acidity, tannin and sugar to enable the end product to achieve a good alcohol content and keep sound and sweet for a year or more.

Some orchards would have a few cherry trees, perhaps a plum and a few eating pears or even perry pear trees – indeed in Gloucestershire and Herefordshire some farm orchards were solely planted with perry pear trees and made perry in lieu of cider.

In our valley in Devon every farm still has an orchard ranging from half an acre to some 3 or 4 acres, so beautiful to the eye in April and May when awash with a great curtain of glorious pink blossom. These orchards were planted between the two world wars, for apple trees do not live for ever – a hundred years would be a very old orchard indeed with many dead and dying trees. Perry pears, growing as they do to a great height and size, live considerably longer. In the past, as an orchard declined, it would have been gradually replanted since it was an important part of the economy of the farm.

For today's would-be home cider maker, consider planting a few cider apple trees in your garden or in your orchard, should you be fortunate enough to have one. Sources of supply of ancient and modern varieties are given in Appendix 2. If you have room for just one tree, Kingston Black is the best in which the apples are vested with all the possible attributes for making a fine single variety cider. Alternatively, sally forth into the depths of the countryside at weekends and ask owners of old farm orchards if they still use their apples, and if not could you collect and take some away for a modest remuneration. You may draw a blank on your first one or more farms, but do continue for many farmers do not use their orchards and would be delighted to either give you the apples in exchange for some cider, or charge a direct rate per sack of fruit.

Mellowing

For cider making, the apples are best allowed to fall on the grass to mellow for a while during which time the water is slowly evaporating and the sugar content is subsequently rising. Leave them to soften for two to three weeks.

Crushing

First check over the apples, washing any muddy ones and discarding the rotten, mouldy fruit and bad specimens to the compost heap. If you are fortunate enough to have an apple mill or crusher, or can borrow one, grind the apples through this into new, clean, flexible polythene dustbins or tubs (*do not* use an old household dustbin – however well cleaned!). If you do not have access to an apple mill, obtain a large, shallow, heavy duty polythene bin, or a small half cask with the bottom filled in so it cannot be knocked out, and a stout 1·5 metre stave which tapers from a wide, flat base to a narrower handle end. Put some of the fruit into the container and proceed to pound it to a fine pulp with the stave; once a few have been broken up the job becomes easier as the mash then holds the subsequent apples so you can smash them more easily.

Pressing

Line the cider press basket with nylon netting. Transfer the pulp to the press basket and stamp it down evenly and firmly, and when full fit the pressure plate. Put one of two well cleaned and sterilised buckets beneath the lip of the press and begin to apply pressure evenly and slowly. A slow pressing will extract more juice than a rapid one. Exchange the bucket when the one beneath the press is full and pour the apple juice into clean, sterilised containers, filling not more than three-quarters full to allow for a possibly vigorous fermentation. Add 30–40 milligrammes per litre of wine sulphur to kill off the wild yeasts.

Test the gravity with a hydrometer in a trial glass; apple juice is usually *c.* 1040 in a poor year and 1050–1060 in a fine sunny year. This reading basically shows the natural sugar content of the juice, the fermentation will convert this sugar into alcohol with the by-product of carbon dioxide given off as a gas through the air lock during the process.

Specific gravity and alcohol

Study the tables on specific gravity and alcohol levels – you will note that a gravity of 1040 or 40 oechsle (oe.) – will give a final alcohol content of approximately 5 per cent by volume. This is not high enough to act as a preservative to enable the finished cider to keep – an alcohol of at least 6 per cent by volume is required so you would have to raise the gravity by adding some cane sugar. You may prefer to raise the gravity/alcohol ratio to 60oe./7·5 per cent alcohol; higher and the product becomes more like wine and ceases to be quaffable by the pint (or half pint!), it becomes unbalanced and the attractive fresh fruity apple flavour becomes swamped by the fiery alcohol content.

Check the table to see how much (if any) sugar you should add to raise the initial natural gravity to make a sound cider. The tables are related to litres rather than pints and gallons since all vessels are tabulated in metric volume nowadays, and sugar is sold in kilogramme packs, so it is a simple matter to:

1. check the amount of cider you have in litres
2. check the gravity
3. refer to the table noting the natural gravity, the gravity you require, and then the kilogrammes or grammes of sugar needed to achieve this, if any.

After the apple juice has stood for twelve hours and the wine sulphur had time to kill off the wild yeasts, add your Tate and Lyle to the liquid, then the yeast. I highly recommend the German SIHA yeast for its superior qualities – quick start; gentle slow ferment; ability to ferment in cold temperatures; settlement of the yeast to a firm shallow cheese enabling every last drop of cider to be drawn off at racking. Swiss Novo yeast is also good.

Prime the air lock and the fermentation will begin in six to eighteen hours, twenty-four at most.

Racking

Watch for the fermentation slowing and finally just about stopping – at this point the clearing cider must be racked off the sediment of dead and dying yeast cells and pulp particles. Syphon the cider off into clean and sterile vessels, this time filling the containers to within about 2·5 centimetres of the cork or bung. The cider may re-activate due to the introduction of oxygen at racking, but this will be a gentle, restrained affair which will subside if the temperatures reach below zero for several days, as they can during January or February, only to begin again when the temperature rises.

When all activity ceases, rack the cider again into clean sterilised vessels, this time filling them right up to the bung so there is little or no air gap.

Air locks

Airlocks must be regularly emptied and refilled with a 2 per cent solution of wine sulphur and water otherwise they will cease to keep the cider free of contamination and the cider will acetify or turn to vinegar.

Bottling

When the cider clears and becomes still, some decisions have to be made. It will remain sound in bulk for one or two years if kept in a cool even temperature battened down with a solid bung. However, you will eventually want to start drinking your cider but you cannot draw off some for consumption and expect the now less than full vessel to remain in good condition – the presence of air will quickly encourage deterioration.

You can, of course, draw off your cider into 5 or 2 litre jars which will remain sound for a week or ten days in a refrigerator.

The other alternative is to put your cider into wine bottles, preferably dark green or golden Burgundy bottles. It is advised that you filter your cider to remove any bacteria or yeast cells before bottling.

Filtering

For the home cider maker a Vinamat filter will tackle the task admirably. This excellent device will, of course, cope equally well with wine.

Buy a pack of twenty-five or fifty coarse filter sheets and twenty-five or fifty sterile pads, according to your output, re-membering that you need two of each per filtration, and one pair of pads will only tackle about five gallons (depending upon clarity) before becoming clogged and useless.

Method. You must coarse filter first so insert a coarse sheet into each half of the filter, pour some wine sulphur solution over each to allow it to swell and form a perfect fit. Carefully position the separator ring and then assemble the unit and screw it tightly together. Now put some wine sulphur solution into the pressure vessel and swill it about to sterilise it, do not forget to sterilise the tubes as well.

Next fill the vessel with clean water and proceed to flush through the system until the filtered water loses its papery taste, 9 or 10 litres may be necessary to achieve this. The wing nuts will probably be able to be tightened further.

Then fill the container with cider and apply pressure gently. Taste the outflow continuously, allowing it to run away until all the water has been flushed and replaced by cider. When you taste that there is much more cider than water, the flushings can be poured back into the bulk, thereby cutting down the losses. Run this coarse filtered cider into clean sterile vessels and close firmly.

When you are ready to bottle, wash the required amount of bottles, and then rinse them with a 2 per cent sulphur solution, turning them upside down to drain before use.

Repeat the preparation process with your Vinamat filter, this time using sterile sheets. By standing the filter on the draining board and having the bottles in the sink, preferably held safely in a bottle carrier, one can quite easily manage the process by oneself provided one has prepared sufficient bottles first and set up the corker and corks in readiness. Ideally, of course, a companion makes life much easier and can look after the corking and binning away of the full bottles. Try to make sure that everything is at hand before starting.

Fill the bottles to within a half inch of where the cork will be when driven home.

Corks

Do not buy the poor quality corks which are so often seen in high street shops, but send off to a reputable cork dealer and importer who will offer a sulphur treating and waxing process so that the corks can be used without any boiling or soaking which renders them either unacceptably hard or soft and porous. I find 'B' grade corks are fine for cider which is a tough product with high acids and tannins, but always use grade 'A' corks for the wine since it is a more delicate product, more susceptible to contamination and spoilage.

Sweet cider

The instructions so far refer to the production of a dry cider. If you want to produce a sweeter drink, two options are open to you. Either you stop the first fermentation at a stage when you like the degree of sweetness, usually at a gravity of between 5 and 10oe. To achieve this the cider is racked off its sediment into clean sterilised vessels and heavily sulphured to suppress further fermentation – add 10 grammes of wine sulphur to each 100 litres of cider (this is approximately two heaped teaspoons). If you have more or less cider, simply work out the ratio and add sulphur accordingly. Stir or shake the cider to make certain the sulphur is thoroughly mixed.

The alternative is to allow the cider to ferment out to dryness, and then sulphur at 10 grammes per 100 litres after having added some highly concentrated sugar/water syrup to taste. Filter and bottle *immediately* after the syrup addition, paying extra special attention to the sterilising of all equipment, bottles, corks etc. to avoid any contamination which could start up a disastrous fermentation in the bottles.

Keep a very careful eye on a sweet cider when bottled for signs of pressure building up behind the corks, shown by seepage or weeping. If this should happen open all the bottles immediately and empty them into clean sterile containers and allow to ferment out before contemplating re-bottling. Trouble is most likely to occur in very hot weather, so do be watchful or you could lose all the results of your hard work.

Small cider

This was the secondary product made in the past for quenching the thirst of haymakers and toilers in the harvest field, a low-alcohol refreshing fruity drink.

Take the pulp from the cider press, put it into a large tub or half cask, breaking it up well. Cover the pulp with cold water and then add 20 grammes per litre of wine sulphur, stirring it in well. After twenty-four hours, bucket or pour the pulp into the cider press which has been lined with a sheet of nylon netting. Pour the resulting juice into clean sterile containers and innoculate with yeast. If the small cider is left without any sugar it will register approximately half the gravity of the first pressing, so it may be necessary to add some Tate and Lyle at this stage to raise the sugar content to a gravity of 50 or 60oe. Now treat similarly to natural cider. The end product will taste similar, but lighter and more delicate, features indeed that many people prefer.

Another way to make a small cider is to once again place the broken up cake removed from the press in a large-topped container, cover with water and sulphur it lightly. Add some SIHA wine yeast, again stirring well, and cover the cask with a lid and an air lock primed with sulphur solution.

Ferment on the apple pulp for seven days to extract colour and flavour, then re-press the pulp and treat as ordinary cider.

Perry

Perry is made from the fermented juice of pears. There are many varieties of specific perry pears that were widely planted in Herefordshire and Gloucestershire in the last century; many farms had large acreages of perry pear trees which grew to a vast size with age, and live many, *many* years longer than apple trees.

It is not everyone who is fortunate enough to be able to use the real perry pear varieties today, so most of us have to make do with dessert and cooking pears. Again, a mixture of strains is the answer for a better end product.

Allow the pears to ripen, but *not* become soft and mushy – the timing is critical here to catch the pears when in exactly the right condition, which lasts only two or three days.

Pears are usually high in sugar but low in acid and tannins, so mix some fairly sharp acidic apples with the pears as they are run through the crusher (75 per cent pears to 25 per cent apples), or crush and press the two separately and mix the juice afterwards at the same rate. This is important or you will finish up with a soft flabby rather undistinguished liquid.

Run the pears through an apple mill into a clean tub, and then tip the pulp into the cider press basket which has been carefully lined with a double layer of butter muslin or nylon curtain netting.

Apply pressure very gently or the pear pulp will blend like wet blancmange and squeeze out through the cloth liner. The apple pulp helps the pear pulp to remain stable by firming up the press contents and allowing the juice to run more freely.

Transfer the juice into a clean sterile container, quickly add wine sulphur at a rate of 5 grammes (one level teaspoon) per 90 litres – a fairly substantial dosage, for pears, being soft and often thin skinned, are more likely to carry bacteria as they are frequently punctured by birds and wasps.

Gravity and acidity

Test the gravity of the juice to find out if an addition of some cane sugar is required. A perry is best finished with an alcohol content of no more than 8 per cent by volume, so have some Tate and Lyle on hand in case it is needed. Consult the table on gravity/ sugar/alcohol content to work out the amount you need to add. If you have facilities for testing the acid, this is an excellent plan for pear juice is usually deficient in acidity, and if none is added to raise the initial acidity to between 9–11 tartaric the perry will not keep for long when made and will taste too soft and flabby. You can add citric acid to a drink destined for home consumption, but not if it is intended for sale. On a very small scale, the juice of two or three lemons per 5 litres will correct the low acid problem.

After sulphuring, leave to stand for twenty-four hours then add some SIHA wine yeast, remembering not to fill the containers more than three-quarters full to allow space for a vigorous fermentation.

Fit a sterilised air lock filled with 2 per cent sulphur solution and with luck fermentation will commence within two to three days – probably sooner.

Rack as the gravity nears zero for a dry perry, and 5 to 10 if you prefer a sweeter finish. Rack into a clean sterile vessel, fill to the top and, for a dry perry, to every 90 litres add 5 grammes of wine sulphur just to keep the beverage sound and clean.

Sweet perry

If you want a sweet perry add 20 grammes of wine sulphur per 90 litres to inhibit any further activity, bung down with a solid cork and either await frosty weather for the cold stabilisation process, or put the perry in the fridge for fourteen days. This should assist clearing and deposition of any solids. Expose both the sweet and the dry perry to this cold treatment.

As soon as you have time prepare to bottle your sweet perry. Retest the free sulphur with a kit you can buy from A. Massel (see Appendix 1), and raise to 50 ppm. Clean and sterilise your Vinamat filter and sufficient bottles, and then filter and bottle immediately. Cork straight away and lay the bottles down in the cool and dark.

After bottling a sweet product, a constant watch must be kept during spring and summer in case corks are expelled due to pressure being built up in the bottles. Some yeast cells may have slipped through the filter and, being excited by the warmth, begun to ferment the residual sugar. Once the hot weather has passed without mishap you can reckon that all is well.

Perry destined to be finished dry will gently ferment on until all the sugar is consumed, when the air lock will cease to move. Rack off into clean sterilised containers, fill to the top and close down firmly until you decide to bottle, preferably in March, April or May.

Test the gravity, and if it is below zero, raise the sulphur level to 30 ppm, clean and sterilise your filter and enough bottles, and then bottle immediately. Cork the bottles and then, if possible, lay them away in the cool and dark.

Perry should be a light, delicate, refreshing beverage, sometimes slightly effervescent and destined to be drunk young and chilled on a warm summer's evening.

List of currently available cider apple trees

Breakwell
Browns Apple*
Brown Snout
Bulmers Norman
Chisel Jersey
Cornish Gillyflower*
Crimson King
Dabinett*
Devonshire Quarendon*
Filbarrel
Foxwhelp

Harry Masters Jersey
Kingston Black
Michelin
Nethou
Sweet Alford*
Sweet Coppin*
Somerset Redstreak*
Taylors Sweet
Tremletts Bitter
Vilberie
Yarlington Mill*

*Especially recommended

List of currently available perry pear trees

Barland
Barnet
Blakeny Red
Butt
Gin
Green Horse
Hellens Early
Hendre Huffcap

Judge Amphlet
Moorcroft
Oldfield
Parsonage
Red Pear
Taynton Squash
Winnalls Longdon
Yellow Huffcap

10. *Liqueur Making*

iqueurs can easily be made at home, provided that you are prepared to buy either gin, whisky or brandy in which the fruits, nuts or herbs are to be steeped in order to extract the flavour. To imitate many of the commercial liqueurs would be impossible as the recipes are usually closely guarded secrets, some having been so for centuries. But to produce a liqueur at home is a relatively simple affair. After washing and drying the fruit for the liqueur, the usual method is to prick holes with a silver or stainless-steel fork all over the skins. They are then packed down firmly either into a Kilner preserving jar (very useful for making small amounts), or a 2.75 litre pickle jar, which has been well washed and sterilised.

Next, a suitable amount of sugar is added, then the jar is topped up with the desired spirit and then well sealed down. The jar should initially be shaken daily to ensure that the sugar does not sink to the bottom but penetrates the fruit and becomes one with the spirit.

After a suitable period of steeping has ensued, the liquid is strained several times through four thicknesses of muslin so that absolute brilliance and clarity are obtained, and then bottled into clean sterile bottles and firmly corked down. It should be allowed to mature at least six months, by which time the results should be mellow and perfect. The spirits being of high alcohol level will prevent the liqueurs from fermenting.

Store the jars and bottles well away from the light, in some dark cupboard, or they will lose colour, remembering to shake the jars daily for the first 2–4 weeks to ensure absorption of the sugar and aid flavour extraction.

There are other fruits from which liqueurs can be made but I have chosen the best and most worthwhile recipes.

One final point – do try and obtain some liqueur bottles in

which to store your efforts: hotels and restaurants throw away dozens of beautifully shaped bottles each week. A liqueur somehow does not seem a liqueur if it is not suitably bottled.

Apricot liqueur

> approx. 20 apricots
> ¼ litre brandy
> 250 g sugar

Cut up the ripe fruit, then, breaking the stones, blanch and crush the kernels. Put the fruit and kernels into a large 50 gramme to 1 kilogramme Kilner jar, plus the sugar, and fill to the top with brandy, or, if preferred, gin. Screw the lid down well and shake the bottle daily if possible for about three weeks, then leave the liqueur to mature for a further five to nine weeks before filtering through muslin and bottling.

Blackcurrant liqueur (cassis)

Fill 50 gramme to 1 kilogramme Kilner jars with clean, topped and tailed, hand-bruised, ripe blackcurrants adding 150 grammes of sugar per half litre of liquid. Lastly, top up the jars with unsweetened gin and screw the tops well down. Shake vigorously each day until the sugar and fruit colouring are thoroughly mixed with the gin, leaving in the jars for about two months before straining and bottling.

Bullace gin

> bullaces
> 170 g sugar
> gin

Fill a Kilner jar with well pricked bullaces, which are little wild black plums. Pour in the sugar and fill the jar with gin. Shake daily for three to four weeks and bottle after two to three months. Over ripe fruit can lead to a liqueur that remains cloudy so only use firm bullaces.

Cherry brandy

    big black or Morello cherries
    250 g caster sugar
    ½ litre brandy
    12 almonds or 6 drops almond essence

Lay alternate layers of clean, pricked cherries and sugar into your jars and then fill up with the brandy, adding the almonds or almond essence. Shake daily until the contents have mixed thoroughly and mature for two to three months.

When making any of these liqueurs either brandy, gin or whisky can be used equally well. The recipe does not have to be rigidly adhered to; I have merely stated the most usual spirit to be used in each case. If you have a preference for gin, for instance, you can use it instead of brandy with the cherries, whisky with blackberries or brandy with blackcurrants.

Cream liqueur

    1 can sweetened condensed milk
    1 can Nestlé thick cream (small)
    3 eggs
    1 tsp. coconut essence
    1 tbsp. Creme de Cacao
    1½ cups Irish whiskey (or Scotch)

Mix the ingredients together and then drink within three to four months.

Damson gin

    500 g–1 kg damsons
    170 g sugar
    ¾ litre gin

After pricking the fruit well with a silver or stainless steel fork, fill the preserving jars with your damsons. Then pour in the sugar

followed by the gin which should come to the top of the jar.
Shake daily for about three weeks and leave for a further five
before straining and bottling.

Egg liqueur

6 fresh eggs
6 lemons
500 g honey
1 gill raw cream
½ bottle of brandy or rum

Wipe the eggs carefully and put them in an earthenware or
polythene bowl with the juice of the six lemons and a tablespoon
of grated rind. Cover well for forty-eight hours or so until the
eggshells have dissolved. Next, add the raw cream, honey, and
the spirit of your choice, stirring until well mixed and then bottle
and cork up firmly.

Lemon liqueur

4 lemons
250 g caster sugar
¾ litre whisky, brandy or gin

Grate the lemon rinds thinly and add this and their juice to
the spirit, plus the caster sugar. Seal up and mature for six to
eight weeks, shaking as often as possible to mix the contents
thoroughly.

Mulberry liqueur

500 g–1 kg sound mulberries
115 g caster sugar
½ litre brandy or gin

Put the mulberries into the jar, adding the sugar, then top up
with whichever spirit you prefer or have on hand. Infuse or steep

for a month or six weeks, strain then bottle – remembering to shake daily during the first three weeks of the steeping period.

Noisette (walnut-skin liqueur)

> skins from fresh green walnuts
> brandy

Fill a Kilner jar(s) with clean, freshly removed green walnut skins and cover with brandy. Infuse for two months, strain and bottle. A great favourite with natives of the Dordogne valley in South West France.

Orange liqueur

Many of the most popular amongst the commercial liqueurs are made from oranges or orange flowers.

> 4–5 Seville oranges
> 250 g caster sugar
> 2 inches of cinnamon stick
> 2 cloves
> ¾ litre brandy

After washing and drying the oranges, grate the rinds very thinly to avoid the white pith which causes bitterness. Put the rind in your jar with the 250 grammes of sugar (or sugar candy may be used) and cover with the spirit. Steep in the jar for two to three months, strain and bottle and *try* to keep it for two years before drinking.

Peach liqueur

> peaches
> 175 g caster sugar
> 175 g brown sugar
> ¾ litre brandy

Fill your large Kilner jar or glass jar with halved, ripe peaches, having removed their stones. Extract a few kernels from the stones, which you add to the fruit plus the sugar and then top up with brandy. Screw down the lid tightly and steep for two to three months, shaking the container daily at first. Filter or strain before bottling through several layers of muslin.

Pineapple liqueur

> pineapple
> caster sugar
> brandy
> 2 cloves
> 5 cm of cinnamon stick

After peeling a ripe, fresh pineapple, cut it into chunks with a stainless steel or silver knife. Fill your jar three-quarters full, allowing 250 grammes of sugar to 500 grammes of fruit. Add the cloves and the cinnamon and then fill up to the top with brandy or gin. Seal tightly and, shaking daily at first, store for two months before straining and bottling.

Plum liqueur

> plums
> sugar
> brandy, rum or gin

Making sure that the plums are ripe but firm and sound, prick them with a needle or fork and half to three-quarters fill your jars, adding 170 grammes caster sugar to 500 grammes of fruit. Fill the bottles up with one of the spirits and seal thoroughly. Shake daily at first and mature for 2–3 months before straining and bottling.

Raspberry liqueur

> 500 g–1 kg raspberries
> 750 g white sugar
> 1 litre brandy or gin

Using only fresh fruit, fill a Kilner jar adding the sugar in alternating layers with the raspberries. Then fill up to the top with brandy, preferably, or gin. Store for two to three months, agitating daily during the first three weeks. Filter through muslin several times before bottling. This makes a really first class liqueur.

Redcurrant liqueur

Amount and recipe the same as for blackcurrant liqueur.

Sloe gin

> 500 g–1 kg sloes
> 85–120 g white sugar
> ¾ litre gin
> 6 almonds or almond essence

Fill the preserving jar or jars with clean, well pricked sloes. Pack the fruit down well, pour in the sugar and either half-a-dozen blanched almonds or a few drops of almond essence. Fill the jar up to the brim with gin and close tightly. Shake daily for three weeks and steep in all for two to three months before filtering and bottling. This makes a wonderfully smooth and warming drink for a cold winter's day.

Strawberry liqueur

> strawberries
> 1 lemon
> sugar
> brandy

Fill a Kilner jar with ripe, sound fruit, add a teaspoon of grated lemon peel and 120 grammes of sugar per 500 grammes of berries. Fill up with brandy and seal down for two to three months, shaking daily for the first week or two. Strain and bottle.

Whitecurrant liqueur

> 500 g– 1 kg whitecurrants
> 120 g sugar

   1 lemon
   ginger essence
   whisky

Having stripped the currants from their stalks, put them into a
jar, adding the sugar, a few small pieces of lemon rind and a small
teaspoon of ginger essence. Lastly fill with whisky and infuse for
two to three months, shaking well daily for the first three weeks.
Filter and bottle.

Appendix 1. *Weights and Measures Conversion Table*

Metric	British
1 millimetre	0·039 inch
1 centimetre	0·394 inch
1 metre	1·094 yards
1 kilometre	0·6214 mile
1 millilitre	0·002 pint
1 centilitre	0·018 pint
1 litre	1·76 pints
1 milligramme	0·015 grain
1 gramme	15·43 grain
1 kilogramme	2·205 pounds

Vine spacing

30 centimetres	1 foot
1.3 metres	4 feet

Vine spraying

4.5 litres	1 gallon
15 litres	3.3 gallons
22.5 litres	5 gallons
28 grammes	1 ounce
55 grammes	2 ounces

Appendix 2 *List of Suppliers*

Casks

Ex-whisky oak casks (25 and 45 gallon sizes)
Highway Cooperage, 79 River Road, Barking, Essex.

Chemical sprays

Sulphur, Zineb, Bravo, Rovral, Mag. Sulph. etc.
Avoncrop Ltd, Nye Road, Sandford, Nr. Bristol.

Cider apple trees

Bulmers, Plough Lane, Hereford.
Scotts Nurseries, Merriot, Nr. Crewkerne, Somerset.

Corks and capsules

J. Perkins & Son, Algarve House, 1 Joan Street, The Cut,
London SE1 8OA.

Fruit presses, crushers, apple mills, bottle fillers, corkers, bottle sterilisers, drainers etc.

Equipment in a wide range of sizes to suit all producers.
Tim Pearkes, Yearlstone Vineyard, Bickleigh, Tiverton, Devon.

Fruit trees, bushes, canes etc.

Highfield Nurseries, Whitminster, Glos.
Scotts Nurseries, Merriot, Nr. Crewkerne, Somerset.

Glass jars, fermentation locks, bungs, hydrometers and hydrometer trial jars, yeast nutrient, grape concentrate etc.

Boots the Chemists, the high street in most British towns.

Vinamat filters and filter sheets

Johnson Home Wine Supplies, 1 The Hornet, Chichester, Sussex.

Vines – white, black, outdoor varieties

Yearlstone Vineyard, Bickleigh, Tiverton, Devon.

Vineyard etc. sprayers

Knapsack, motorised knapsack, self-propelled and trailer models.
Hardi Ltd, St George's Way, Bermuda Industrial Estate, Nuneaton, Worcs.

Vineyard sundries – also wine chemicals

Hooks, chains, anchor discs, augers, tie-guns etc.
David Cowderoy, Rock Lodge Vineyard, Scaynes Hill, Hayward's Heath, Sussex.

Wine bottles

Delivered on pallets of *c.* 625 bottles or in boxes of 1 dozen.
Rawlings & Son (Bristol) Ltd, Cecil Road, Bristol BS15 2NA.

Wine filters and pumps, bottle fillers, large wine tanks

A. Massel & Co. Ltd, Woodlands, Hazel Grove, Hindhead, Surrey.

Wine testing kits and all wine chemicals

In 1 kg packs and larger amounts.
A. Massel & Co. Ltd, Woodlands, Hazel Grove, Hindhead, Surrey.

Wine vats in polyethylene from Germany

From 60 to 2000 litres capacity.
Dept GP, Tapestry Vineyard, Wells Farm, Apperly, Gloucester.
(Order before July for August/September delivery).

Wine yeast

H. E. Lunken & Co. Ltd, Unit 8, Kings Yard, Carpenters Road London E15 2HD.

Bibliography

Baker, H., *Fruit* (Mitchell Beazley, 1980)

Berry, Cyril J. J., *Winemaker's Companion* (Argus Books, 1987)

Duncan, P. and Acton, A., *Making Wines Like Those You Buy* (Argus Books, 1968)

Pearkes, G., *Vinegrowing in Britain* (J. M. Dent and Son Ltd, 1982)

Sampson, B., *The Art of Making Wine* (Aurum Press Ltd, 1987)

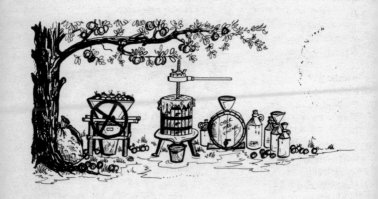

Index

acid 29
Acidex 29, 88
acidity 29, 57
acid testing kit 31
alcohol 54
apples 34, 40, 47, 56
apple rootstocks 34
apricot liquer 108
apricots 36, 40, 56
Auxerrois 73, 80

Bacchus 82
bananas 57
Barland 106
Barnet 106
Benlate 51, 72, 74
bilberries 56
bittersharps 96
bittersweets 96
blackberries 40, 45, 49, 56
blackcurrant liqueur 108
blackcurrants 15, 37, 40, 45, 48, 56
Blakeney Red 106
Blauberger 85
body 57
Boron 72
Botrytis 51, 70, 71, 72, 73
bottles 25, 61
bottling 22, 61
Bravo 51, 72, 74
Breakwell 106
Brewbelt 28
broom flowers 59
Browns Apple 106

Brown Snout 106
budburst (vines) 76
Bullace gin 108
Bulmers Norman 106
Butt 106

Campden tablets 54
Cane sugar 19
capsule 26
Cassis 108
charcoal 31
Chardonnay 73, 80, 81, 82
Chempro SDP 23, 26
cherry brandy 109
cherries 40, 45, 56
Chisel Jersey 106
chlorine 22, 26
cider 95
citric acid 3, 57
clover 59
cold stabilisation 21
copper 71, 76
cool steeping 15, 54
cordons 35, 44
corks 25, 101
Cornish Gillyflower 106
Cox's Orange Pippin 35
cream liqueur 109
Crimson King 106
crushing apples 97
Cuprokylt 72, 75

Dabinet 35, 106
damson gin 109
damsons 43, 56

Derris 51
Devonshire Quarrendon 106
disbudding (vines) 76, 79
Dithane 495 46
docks 79
Dornfelder 86

Early Rivers 45
egg liqueur 110
Ehrenfelser 73, 82, 84
elderberries 56
elderflowers 57, 59
Elvaron 72, 74
espaliers 35, 44

fans 45
fermentation lock 19
flower wines 58
Filbarrel 106
filtration 22, 100
Foxwhelp 106
fruit wines 53
Fungex 72, 73

German polythene tanks 21
Gewurtztraminer 81
gin 106
gooseberries 15, 40, 46, 47, 49,
   56
Gooseberry Sawfly 51
grape crusher 87
grapes 47
grape winemaking 87
gravity 54
greengages 56
Green Horse 106
Guyot 67

Harry Masters Jersey 106
harvesting (grapes) 80
Hellens Early 106

hen and chickens 85
Hendre Huffcap 106
Honey Fungus 51
hot steeping 15
Huxelrebe 73, 83
hydrometer 20, 31, 87, 98
hydrometer trial jar 31

immersion heater 28

James Grieve 35
Judge Amphlet 106
juice extraction 15

Kerner 73, 83, 84
Kingston Black 35, 96, 196
Kiwi fruit 36

labels 26
lemon liqueur 110
lemons 19, 54, 55, 67
Leon Millot 67, 73, 85
liqueurs 107

Madeleine Angevine 73, 81, 82,
   84
Madeleine Sylvaner 73, 81, 82,
   90
maidens 35
maiden tree 38
Merryweather 45
Michelin 106
Millerandage 85
Moorcraft 106
Moorpark 40
mulberry liqueur 110
mullberries 56
Muller Thurgau 73

Nectarines 40
Nethou 106

nettles 79
Nicotine 51
nitrogen 37
noisette 111
Novo yeast 88, 99
nutrition 36, (vines) 80

Oidium 70, 71
Oldfield 106
Optima 83
orange liqueur 111
oranges 56
Ortega 90

Parsonage 106
peach liqueur 111
peaqches 40, 56
peach leaf curl 46
Pectozyme 16
perry 103
perry pears 96, 106
photosynthesis 36, 64, 77, 80
pineapple liqueur 112
Pinot Gris 73, 80, 81
Pinot Meunier 80, 82
Pinot Noir 73, 80, 81, 82
Pixie rootstock 46
plum liqueur 112
plums 40, 46, 56
pollen 36
pollination 35
post-blossom spray (vines) 77
Potassium metabisulphite 17, 18, 22, 54
Potassium sorbate 22, 27, 31
powdery mildew 47, 70, 71
primroses 59
pre-blossom spray (vines) 76, 78
pressing 16, 97
pruning 47

Purple Pershore 46
Pyrethrum 51

racking 89, 92, 99
raspberry beetle 51
raspberry liqueur 112
raspberries 15, 40, 46, 50, 56
redcurrant liqueur 113
redcurrants 56
red pear 106
red wine (grape) 91, 92, 93
Reichensteiner 73, 82, 83
Riesling 83, 84
rootstocks 33, 34
rosehips 56
Roundup 79
Rovral 51, 72, 73, 74
Rubigan 47, 51
Rulander 81

Scheurebe 83, 84
Seyval Blanc 82, 84
Sharps 96
sideshooting (vines) 77
Sigerrebe 73, 82, 84, 90, 93
SIHA yeast 17, 18, 28, 88, 99, 104
Silver Birch sap wine 62
silver leaf fungus 47
Sloe Gin 113
sloes 56
small cider 95, 102
spraying 47, (vines) 70, 71
strawberry liqueur 113
strawberries 40, 56
stuck fermentation 28, 30
sugar 54
sulphate of potash 36, 80
sulphur 29, 70, 71, 76, 90
sulphur test kit 31
Superphosphate 36, 80

Sweet Alford 106
Sweet Coppin 106
sweet cider 101
sweet perry 104
sweet reserve 90, 91
sweets 96

tannin 57
Tate & Lyle 28, 54, 88, 91, 92, 93
tar oil 71
tayberries 49
Taylors Sweet 106
Taynton Squash 106
thistles 79
training 47, (vines) 68, 69, 76
Tremletts Bitter 106
Triomphe d'Alsace 67, 73, 85

Vilberie 106
Vinamat filter 23, 31, 61, 100,
    101
vine nutrition 80
vine spraying 70, 71
vine training 68, 69, 76
vine trellis 66, 67, 69
vineyard 64

Vinifera 67
vinometer 31

weed control (vines) 79
weights & measures conversion
    115
whitecurrant liqueur 113
whitecurrants 56
white wines (grape) 88, 89, 90,
    91, 93
wild yeasts 18, 27, 98
winter pruning (vines) 75, 78
wine chemical store 30
winemaker's garden 32
wine press 87
wine sulphur 17, 18, 22, 54
Winnals Longdon 106
woodashes 36

Yarlington Mill 106
yeast 17, 54, 55
yeast nutrient 54, 55
Yellow Huffcap 106

Zineb 70, 71, 76
Zweigeltrebe 85

ALICE KING

Winewise

How to be streetwise about wine

How many times have you wished you knew what wine to order in a restaurant, or which bottle to buy from the numerous shelves in the supermarket?

Written in a lively, amusing and utterly unpompous way, WINEWISE dispels all the snobbery and myths about wine.

To be Winewise, you need to know the basic tricks of the trade: which wines to look out for and when, which to use as a benchmark on a restaurant wine list, which cheap wines to go for and which to avoid. You need to know how you can deduce the contents of a bottle by its shape; what type of wine glasses to choose; when to use decanters and when not; how to read a label; how to taste and what goes best with the food you're eating. And you will also discover here all the important wine-growing regions, their characteristics and their best bargains.

WINEWISE will give encouragement and confidence to any-one who buys wine, would like to know more about it, but who believes, above all, that wine-drinking is fun.

Alice King is Britain's youngest nationally read wine writer.

'Enlivened by the author's appetisingly anecdotal approach.' Jancis Robinson, *Evening Standard*

JANCIS ROBINSON

The Demon Drink

'Every intelligent drinker owes it to his (and, particularly, her) liver, and gut, and brain, and children, to find out more about alcohol and about whether they fall into any of the particularly high-risk groups, which include such disparate categories as those with a small frame, an ulcer, high blood pressure, or a job on a boat.'

Alcohol is our favourite drug. Used properly, it is a pleasure central to millions of lives. Used unwisely, it can become a substance more dangerous than most of us realize. As members of a culture in which alcohol plays such an important part, we actually know surprisingly little about it.

Hence this book, providing the first genuinely objective and comprehensive information about exactly how much of a demon drink really is. Drink can, indeed, be a wonderful thing. The aim of this book is to celebrate that fact, while placing alcohol in perspective and, most importantly, encouraging a new respect for it.

'It's not an anti-alcohol book, more a user's guide to the true pros and cons of drinking.' *Daily Mail*

'Jancis Robinson is our cleverest, most thoughtful wine writer. In *The Demon Drink*, she has anticipated what are certain to become the most crucial issues for those who really care about wine . . . It will probably turn out to be one of her most important books.' *Observer*

'Beautifully written and awash with sobering facts about alcohol as part of our lives, the book is nonetheless cheerily encouraging as to the benefits of modest tippling as well as being unpatronisingly frank about the all-too-real dangers of overdoing it.' *Ideal Home*

DAVID BOLTON

Journey Without End

'There is something elusive and compelling about the waterways that urges you back and back again.'

David Bolton and Lynda Rolfe decided to throw up their jobs in central London and explore the rest of England in a seventy-foot narrowboat called *Frederick*, traditional in style yet luxuriously equipped.

From the Nene at Peterborough to the Mersey at Ellesmere Port and into the deep south-west at Gloucester and Sharpness, they spent eighteen months covering the inland waterways, mooring near beautiful Oxford colleges and grimy city docks. We share the acquaintance of the many different people they met, including those who still remember life on the old working boats; the unique view of landscape, townscape and wildlife; the problems of breakdown and the pleasures of life on the water.

'Makes you ache for the sound of the wind in the willows.' *Daily Mail*

'Enthralling and absorbing . . . stands head and shoulders above other "Living and cruising on a boat" publications.' *Canal and Riverboat*

'Rich with the gentle pleasures of cruising.' *Books*

A Selected List of Non-Fiction Available from Mandarin Books

While every effort is made to keep prices low, it is sometimes necessary to increase prices at short notice. Mandarin Paperbacks reserves the right to show new retail prices on covers which may differ from those previously advertised in the text or elsewhere.

The prices shown below were correct at the time of going to press.

☐	7493 0000 0	**Moonwalk**	Michael Jackson	£3.99
☐	7493 0004 3	**South Africa**	Graham Leach	£3.99
☐	7493 0010 8	**What Fresh Hell is This?**	Marion Meade	£3.99
☐	7493 0011 6	**War Games**	Thomas Allen	£3.99
☐	7493 0013 2	**The Crash**	Mihir Bose	£4.99
☐	7493 0014 0	**The Demon Drink**	Jancis Robinson	£4.99
☐	7493 0015 9	**The Health Scandal**	Vernon Coleman	£4.99
☐	7493 0016 7	**Vietnam – The 10,000 Day War**	Michael Maclear	£3.99
☐	7493 0049 3	**The Spycatcher Trial**	Malcolm Turnbull	£3.99
☐	7493 0022 1	**The Super Saleswoman**	Janet Macdonald	£4.99
☐	7493 0023 X	**What's Wrong With Your Rights?**	Cook/Tate	£4.99
☐	7493 0024 8	**Mary and Richard**	Michael Burn	£3.50
☐	7493 0061 2	**Voyager**	Yeager/Rutan	£3.99
☐	7493 0060 4	**The Fashion Conspiracy**	Nicholas Coleridge	£3.99
☐	7493 0027 2	**Journey Without End**	David Bolton	£3.99
☐	7493 0028 0	**The Common Thread**	Common Thread	£4.99

All these books are available at your bookshop or newsagent, or can be ordered direct from the publisher. Just tick the titles you want and fill in the form below.

Mandarin Paperbacks, Cash Sales Department, PO Box 11, Falmouth, Cornwall TR10 9EN.

Please send cheque or postal order, no currency, for purchase price quoted and allow the following for postage and packing:

UK	55p for the first book, 22p for the second book and 14p for each additional book ordered to a maximum charge of £1.75.
BFPO and Eire	55p for the first book, 22p for the second book and 14p for each of the next seven books, thereafter 8p per book.
Overseas Customers	£1.00 for the first book plus 25p per copy for each additional book.

NAME (Block Letters) ....

ADDRESS ....

....